QMC
361870 2
a30213 003618702b

D0351690



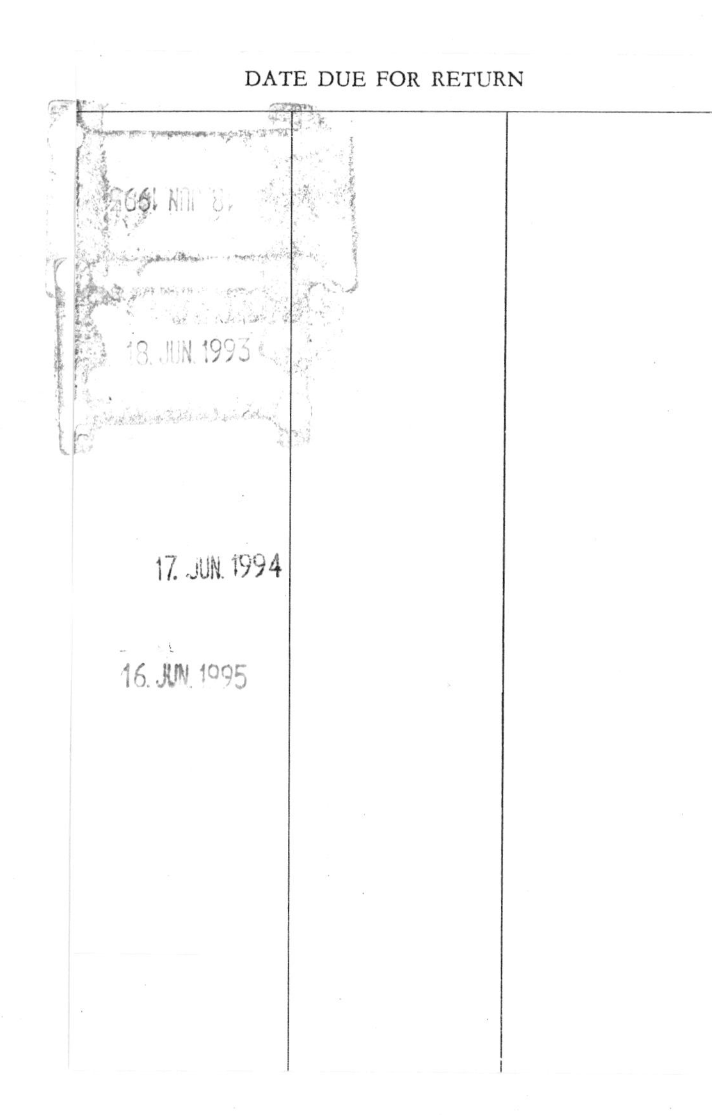
18. JUN. 1993
17. JUN. 1994
16. JUN. 1995

# ARISTOTLE'S MODAL SYLLOGISMS

# STUDIES IN LOGIC

## AND

## THE FOUNDATIONS OF MATHEMATICS

---

L. E. J. BROUWER
E. W. BETH
A. HEYTING

*Editors*

1963

---

NORTH-HOLLAND PUBLISHING COMPANY
AMSTERDAM

# ARISTOTLE'S MODAL SYLLOGISMS

STORRS McCALL
*Assistant Professor of Philosophy*
*McGill University*

1963

NORTH-HOLLAND PUBLISHING COMPANY
AMSTERDAM

PRINTED IN THE NETHERLANDS

# PREFACE

"Who would desire now to oppress the Student with the heavy burden of modals?" So wrote Mansel in the preface to Aldrich's Logic in 1849, and if any excuse be needed, one hundred years later, for adding to this burden it could be found in the modern revival of interest in modal logic. Nor is the book directed at the already-oppressed Student in any case: it represents simply a desire on the part of the author to get straight about a rather obscure segment of Aristotle's logic.

To my colleagues at McGill I am indebted for discussion of many points, and for the patience which they showed in dealing with the many mimeographed drafts of this book. Among those who helped me, I wish particularly to thank Professors Raymond Klibansky of McGill, Arthur Prior of Manchester, Nicholas Rescher of Pittsburgh, and Mr. Michael Dummett of Oxford, all of whom made helpful suggestions on parts of the manuscript, and Mr. André Gombay, of McGill, who read the proofs. Lastly I salute the work of W. D. Ross and Jan Łukasiewicz on the *Prior Analytics*. Without it, this book could scarcely have been written.

STORRS MCCALL

*Montreal*
*18 June 1962*

## NOTATION

The logical symbolism used in this book is based on that of the Polish school. Thus we have:

| | | |
|---|---|---|
| $Np$ | for | not $p$ |
| $Cpq$ | | if $p$ then $q$ |
| $Kpq$ | | $p$ and $q$ |
| $Epq$ | | $p$ if and only if $q$ |
| $Mp$ | | it is possible that $p$ |
| $Lp$ | | it is necessary that $p$ |
| $Qp$ | | it is contingent that $p$. |

In addition, for the premisses of Aristotle's syllogisms we use:

| | | |
|---|---|---|
| $Aab$ | for | all $a$ is $b$ |
| $Eab$ | | no $a$ is $b$ |
| $Iab$ | | some $a$ is $b$ |
| $Oab$ | | some $a$ is not $b$. |

For clarity, separations will be made in formulae containing the latter expressions. Thus $E\ Eab\ NIab$ is to be read: " 'No $a$ is $b$' is equivalent to 'It is not the case that some $a$ is $b$' ".

## CONTENTS

Preface . . . . . . . . . . . . . . . . . . . . . V
Notation . . . . . . . . . . . . . . . . . . . . VI

*Chapter I*

The problem of the apodeictic moods

1. Introduction . . . . . . . . . . . . . . . . . 1
2. Historical survey . . . . . . . . . . . . . . . 1
3. Aristotle's system of apodeictic syllogisms . . . . . . 5
4. Aristotle on the two Barbaras . . . . . . . . . . . 10
5. Hintikka's dilemma . . . . . . . . . . . . . . . 13
6. Theophrastus and Łukasiewicz on the two Barbaras . . 15
7. Concrete examples of the two Barbaras . . . . . . . . 16
8. The Becker approach and its congeners . . . . . . . . 18
9. Rescher's interpretation . . . . . . . . . . . . . 22
10. Completion of Rescher's interpretation . . . . . . . . 25

*Chapter II*

The system of apodeictic moods

11. Systematization of the assertoric moods . . . . . . . 28
12. Modal logic of propositions . . . . . . . . . . . . 30
13. Opposition of modal premisses . . . . . . . . . . . 33
14. Axiomatization of the apodeictic moods. The $L$–$X$–$M$ calculus . . . . . . . . . . . . . . . . . . 36
15. The laws of subalternation . . . . . . . . . . . . 38
16. The laws of conversion . . . . . . . . . . . . . . 39
17. The laws of modal subordination . . . . . . . . . . 41

18. The *LLL*, *LXL* and *XLL* moods . . . . . . . . . . . 41
19. Further *L–X–M* moods . . . . . . . . . . . . . . . . 44

*Chapter III*

DECISION PROCEDURE FOR THE APODEICTIC MOODS

20. The mechanism of rejection . . . . . . . . . . . . . 47
21. A decision procedure for the *L–X–M* calculus . . . . . 51

*Chapter IV*

THE CONTINGENT MOODS

22. General remarks. The contingency operator . . . . . . 66
23. Conversion and opposition of contingent premisses . . . 70
24. Can contingency be defined in terms of possibility and necessity? . . . . . . . . . . . . . . . . . . 72
25. Axiomatization of the contingent moods. The *Q–L–X–M* calculus . . . . . . . . . . . . . . . . . . . 75
26. The laws of complementary conversion . . . . . . . . 78
27. The laws of subalternation . . . . . . . . . . . . . 80
28. The laws of ordinary conversion . . . . . . . . . . . 81
29. The laws of modal subordination . . . . . . . . . . 82
30. Conspectus of Aristotle's contingent moods . . . . . . 83
31. The *QQQ* moods . . . . . . . . . . . . . . . . . 86
32. The *QXQ* and *XQQ* moods . . . . . . . . . . . . . 88
33. The *QXM* and *XQM* moods . . . . . . . . . . . . 89
34. The *QLQ* and *LQQ* moods . . . . . . . . . . . . . 91
35. The *QLX* and *LQX* moods . . . . . . . . . . . . . 91
36. The *QLM* and *LQM* moods . . . . . . . . . . . . . 92
37. Summary of the *Q–L–X–M* moods . . . . . . . . . . 93
38. Conclusion . . . . . . . . . . . . . . . . . . . . 95

INDEX . . . . . . . . . . . . . . . . . . . . . . . . 99

CHAPTER I

# THE PROBLEM OF THE APODEICTIC MOODS

## 1. Introduction

Aristotle's system of modal syllogisms, to be found in chapters 3 and 8–22 of the first book of the *Prior Analytics*, has been open to public inspection for over 2300 years. And yet perhaps no other piece of philosophical writing has had such consistently bad reviews. Beginning with Aristotle's successor Theophrastus ("he of the graceful style"), and continuing through to the modern logician Jan Łukasiewicz, this part of the Philosopher's teachings has been alternately the subject of enthusiastic rebuttal and unjustified neglect. In extenuation, two things must be admitted. Firstly, the subject is of extreme difficulty: there is a mediaeval saying warning that "*De modalibus non gustabit asinus*". Secondly, Aristotle's treatment of modal syllogisms has its share of what may with charity be called obscurities, without charity errors. The present author does no more than claim to find a smaller number of errors and a greater degree of consistency in the work than the majority of his predecessors.

## 2. Historical survey

The fate which Aristotle's modal syllogisms have suffered at the hands of their expositors and critics has not in general been a kind one. Łukasiewicz's judgement is that, in contrast to his assertoric syllogistic, "Aristotle's modal syllogistic is almost incomprehensible because of its many faults and inconsistencies" [1], and this, or something milder, must have been the opinion of the numerous

[1] *Aristotle's Syllogistic*, 2nd ed., Oxford 1957, p. 133.

philosophers who have tried to reform the system since its appearance sometime in the period 350–344 B.C., i.e. in Aristotle's late thirties [1]. We learn from Alexander (*fl.c.* 205 A.D.) [2] that the followers of Theophrastus and Eudemus disagreed with Aristotle's views on which modal syllogistic moods were, and which were not, valid. The precise nature of the disagreement will be discussed in sect. 6. We should be in a better position to judge of the rights and wrongs of the case if Alexander's lost work, *On the Disagreement concerning Mixed Moods between Aristotle and his Friends*, had survived, but as it is we must rely on the work of scholars like Father Bochenski, who in a book which reads like a detective story is able to reconstruct a large part of Theophrastus' logic from clues found in other ancient authors [3].

In the hands of the early Christian scholars modal syllogisms did not fare very well. Writing about 910, the Arabic philosopher al-Farabi said:

> "And so the teaching of Aristotelian logic ... remained in Alexandria, until the Christian emperor concerned himself about it and the bishops met and deliberated as to what part of the Teaching should continue and what should be abolished. They decided that there should only be instruction in the Books of Logic up to the end of the figures of the assertoric syllogisms, and not in that which comes after this, for they were of the opinion, that herein lay a danger to Christianity, but that aid towards the victory of their faith resided in that part in which they permitted instruction. The public (exoteric) part of the Teaching was therefore confined to that limit, while the study of the rest was carried on in private (esoterically), until the rise of Islam much later" [4].

In fact, not only its modal part, but the whole of the *Prior Analytics* disappeared from general circulation in the western

---

[1] The date is W. D. Ross's: see his *Aristotle's Prior and Posterior Analytics*, Oxford 1949, p. 23.

[2] Alexander of Aphrodisias, *In Aristotelis Anal. Pr. I. Commentarium*, ed. Wallies, Berlin 1883.

[3] I. Bochenski, *La logique de Théophraste* (LT), Fribourg 1947.

[4] The quotation is to be found in Nicholas Rescher, *Aristotle's theory of modal syllogisms and its interpretation*, in M. Bunge (ed.) *The Critical Approach: Essays in honor of Karl Popper*, Glencoe Ill., 1963, sect. II.

world until the time of Abailard (1079–1142), when upon its re-emergence it came to be known as the New Logic.

There was, however, considerable interest in modal syllogistic among the Arabic philosophers. Avicenna (979–1037) treated of the modal syllogism at length, upholding Aristotle's theory against both Theophrastus' *peiorem* rule (see sect. 6), and Galen, who, according to Avicenna, maintained the impossibility of there being a scientific treatment of syllogisms with contingent premisses [1]. Averroes (1126–98) wrote three commentaries on the *Prior Analytics,* the middle-sized one of which contains 90 pages devoted to an exposition of modal syllogisms. Averroes' commentaries were followed by, among others, that of Albert the Great (1193–1280), by a commentary attributed to Duns Scotus but in fact by an unknown Scotist, and by that of William of Occam (*c.* 1295–1349).

For those authors who followed Abailard, the distinction between modalities *de dicto* and *de re* was an essential one [2]; for them, the propositions "It is necessary (possible) that *A* is *B*", and "*A* is necessarily (possibly) *B*" differed not only in form but in meaning. In the first case necessity (or possibility) is predicated of a *dictum, de dicto*; in the second case of a thing, *de re.* Or again, in the first case the proposition "*A* is *B*" is said to be "affected" by the mode *in sensu composito;* in the second case *in sensu diviso.* By applying this distinction to the premisses of modal syllogisms, the mediaeval philosophers were able to generate many more syllogistic moods than was Aristotle. Bochenski, who has studied the matter extensively, estimates that the total number of such moods held to be valid by Occam might reach one thousand [3].

Modal syllogistic did not, however, retain a permanent place in logical textbooks. More recent manuals, such as the Port-Royal

---

[1] See I. Madkour, *L'Organon d'Aristote dans le monde arabe,* Paris 1934, pp. 211–12.

[2] It appears that Abailard may have been the originator of this distinction: see W. and M. Kneale, *The Development of Logic,* Oxford 1962, p. 212. Abailard did not himself devote much space to modal syllogisms.

[3] See Bochenski, *Notes historiques sur les propositions modales* (NHPM), Revue des Sciences phil. et théol., 1937, p. 692, and *A History of Formal Logic* (HFL), Notre Dame 1961, p. 224 ff.

logic (1662), Aldrich's compendium (1691), Whately's *Elements of Logic* (1826) and Keynes's *Formal Logic* (1884), contain no account of the modal syllogism. Those which do tend to refer to former treatments of it rather than treat of it themselves. Thus Thomas Reid reports that Keckermann (*fl.* 1600) called the doctrine of the modals the *crux Logicorum*, and doubted whether the Scholastic doctors "tortured most the modal syllogisms, or were most tortured by them". Reid himself decides to let modal syllogistic "rest in peace, without giving the least disturbance to its ashes" [1].

It is not until we come to Albrecht Becker's study and interpretation of Aristotle's system that we find any real gain in understanding [2]. Becker uses the modern symbolism of quantifiers and modal operators to make precise the Scholastic distinction between modal propositions *de dicto* and *de re*, and then attempts to show that Aristotle vacillates between the two limbs of this distinction in interpreting those propositions which serve as the premisses of his modal syllogisms. Becker's approach will be discussed in sect. 8.

To Łukasiewicz we owe the first attempt to set forth modal syllogistic as a completely formalized deductive system. Previously, in 1939, this author had succeeded in axiomatizing the moods of the categorical syllogism on the basis of four axioms, and in 1957 he published his system of the modal moods, adding to his four syllogistic axioms only axioms drawn from the modal logic of propositions [3]. Łukasiewicz's system cannot but be admired as an intellectual *tour de force:* he was compelled, he tells us, to construct an entirely new system of propositional modal logic in order to do justice to Aristotle's insights [4]. Nevertheless Łukasiewicz failed, in fact did not attempt, to reproduce Aristotle's system exactly. This will be shown in detail below.

The most sympathetic treatment of modal syllogisms in recent

---

[1] *A Brief Account of Aristotle's Logic*, 1774. Reprinted in his *Works*, 4th ed., Edinburgh 1854. Quotations from p. 703.

[2] A. Becker-Freyseng, *Die aristotelische Theorie der Möglichkeitsschlüs* (ATM), Berlin 1933.

[3] See Łukasiewicz, introduction and p. 133 ff.

[4] This system appeared separately in a paper in The Journal of Computi Systems, July 1953.

times is Rescher's [1]. This author discusses the attempts of Becker and Łukasiewicz to reconstrue Aristotle's system using the methods of modern symbolic logic, and describes them all as meeting with "utter failure". Though himself a symbolic logician, Rescher implies that any such future attempts must fail also, and offers his own intuitive and non-formal interpretation of the modal moods. I agree with Rescher that previous formal treatments of Aristotle's system have failed, but nonetheless feel that a better treatment can be produced. In fact I shall present a formalized system which I believe agrees exactly with Aristotle's at all important points. With Rescher's intuitive interpretation I have no quarrel; on the contrary it provides the basis for what I believe to be the only satisfactory explanation of the *rationale* of modal syllogisms so far forthcoming.

Rescher apart, then, the overall judgement of philosophers to date on Aristotle's system has been unfavourable. Thus Bochenski:

> "In general one gets the impression that (Aristotle's) modal logic, by contrast to the assertoric syllogistic, is still only in a preliminary and incomplete stage of development" [2].

Yet although Łukasiewicz wrote in order to "explain the difficulties and correct the errors" in Aristotle, it is impossible not to feel that a formal system which follows Aristotle's own logical insights more closely could be constructed. It will be my aim to do this.

## 3. Aristotle's system of apodeictic syllogisms

In order to understand more fully the differences between Aristotle and his successors, I shall present in this section a brief account of the former's system of syllogisms with necessary premisses. Beginning with moods with two necessary premisses, Aristotle maintains that a necessary conclusion follows in exactly those cases in which an assertoric conclusion follows from two

---

[1] *Op. cit.*

[2] Bochenski, HFL, p. 88.

assertoric premisses. He says [1]: "There is hardly any difference between syllogisms from necessary premisses and syllogisms from premisses which merely assert. When the terms are put in the same way, then, whether something belongs or necessarily belongs (or does not belong) to something else, a syllogism will or will not result alike in both cases, the only difference being the addition of the expression 'necessarily' to the terms". Let us take as an example the first-figure mood with universal affirmative premisses, traditionally known as Barbara [2]. In order to distinguish the Barbara with two necessary premisses and necessary conclusion from the ordinary assertoric Barbara, I shall call the former Barbara *LLL*, and the latter Barbara *XXX*. We may state Barbara *LLL* as follows, bearing in mind Łukasiewicz's insistence that Aristotle always states his syllogistic moods in the form of a conditional proposition [3], and disregarding for the moment the distinction between premisses *de dicto* and *de re*, which we shall return to in sect. 13:

| | |
|---|---|
| If | All *B* is necessarily *A* |
| and | All *C* is necessarily *B* |
| then | All *C* is necessarily *A*. |

---

[1] *An. pr.* 29b36–30a1. Except where otherwise noted, the Oxford trans lation will be used throughout this book.

[2] I shall designate by their traditional names, found in but older than Peter of Spain's *Summulae Logicales*, the 14 valid moods of the assertoric syllogism distinguished by Aristotle. They are, in the three figures:

First figure: Barbara, Celarent, Darii, Ferio.

Second figure: Cesare, Camestres, Festino, Baroco.

Third figure: Darapti, Felapton, Disamis, Datisi, Bocardo, Ferison.

See Bochenski, HFL p. 210 ff., for an account of the origin of these names.

[3] Łukasiewicz, p. 2. Other authors have rightly disagreed with Łukasiewicz on this matter: see J. L. Austin's review of *Aristotle's Syllogistic* in Mind (1952), pp. 397–8, where examples of syllogisms in the form of an inference rather than of an implication are given, and A. N. Prior, *Formal Logic*, Oxford 1955, p. 116. Łukasiewicz himself is not consistent on this point, for occasionally he uses "premiss" and "conclusion" where he should be using "antecedent" and "consequent". With these reservations, I shall follow Łukasiewicz's usage, bearing in mind that if the implication is true, the rule of inference follows by the use of *modus ponens*.

We should note that the word "necessarily" in the last line indicates that the conclusion is a necessary proposition, not that it follows necessarily from the premisses. Aristotle is aware of this distinction between the two uses of the word "necessary": see for example 30b31–33, where, speaking of another mood, he says that "one might show ... that the conclusion is not necessary without qualification, though it is a necessary conclusion from the premisses".

Proceeding now to moods with one necessary and one categorical premiss, which are discussed in chapters 9–11 of the first book of the *Prior Analytics*, we find that Aristotle's doctrine concerning them is at once more complicated and more interesting. Here a necessary conclusion follows, but not in every case, as is exemplified by the difference between Barbara *LXL*:

| | |
|---|---|
| If | All *B* is necessarily *A* |
| and | All *C* is *B* |
| then | All *C* is necessarily *A*, |

and Barbara *XLL:*

| | |
|---|---|
| If | All *B* is *A* |
| and | All *C* is necessarily *B* |
| then | All *C* is necessarily *A*. |

Of these the first only, and not the second, is held to be valid by Aristotle. For the validity of the first he does not give any proof (though see sect. 4, in which possible proofs are explored), and we may take it that he assumes Barbara *LXL* to be a "perfect" (undemonstrated) syllogism. For Barbara *XLL*, however, he gives two disproofs; one in which he shows, by an argument resembling *reductio ad absurdum* [1], that a falsehood results from assuming that the conclusion does follow, and one in which he produces a specific example of Barbara *XLL*, with the concrete terms "in movement", "animal" and "man" substituted for the letters *A*,

[1] For a discussion of this method of disproof, which Aristotle also uses for Camestres *LXL* and Cesare *XLL*, see sect. 4.

*B* and *C* respectively. Thus:

| | |
|---|---|
| If | All animals are in movement |
| and | All men are necessarily animals |
| then | All men are necessarily in movement. |

Here the premisses are true and the conclusion false, for "an animal does not move necessarily, nor does man" (30a31), and hence Barbara *XLL* is invalid. This disproof will be considered further in sect. 6.

With one exception, the remaining 26 *LXL* and *XLL* moods are each investigated separately by Aristotle, and, if the mood is not a perfect one, a proof or disproof of validity given. The method of proof is by conversion. For example, by converting the major premiss of Cesare *LXL* (for the rules of conversion of modal premisses see sect. 16), we are able to reduce it to the perfect Celarent *LXL:*

| | | |
|---|---|---|
| If | Necessarily no *A* is *B* | |
| and | All *C* is *B* | Cesare *LXL* |
| then | Necessarily no *C* is *A* | |

| | | |
|---|---|---|
| If | Necessarily no *B* is *A* | |
| and | All *C* is *B* | Celarent *LXL* |
| then | Necessarily no *C* is *A* | |

One further method of proof, used only for the moods Baroco *LLL* and Bocardo *LLL*, is the method of "ecthesis". For details of this method see *An. pr.* 30a6–14, and Ross p. 32 [1]. Two further methods of disproof, in addition to the two used for Barbara *XLL*, are (i) the reduction by conversion of a mood to another mood already shown to be invalid [2], and (ii) the lack of a method of *proving* the conclusion by *reductio ad absurdum*.

I shall not discuss the remaining apodeictic moods individually

[1] It appears that Aristotle might have made much more extensive use of this method than he did. See P. Henle, *On the Fourth Figure of the Syllogism*, Philosophy of Science 14 (1949), p. 99, where proofs by ecthesis are given for Baroco *XLL*, Datisi *XLL*, Disamis *LXL* and Bocardo *LXL*.

[2] For a discussion of Aristotle's use of this method see sect. 20.

but summarize the results Aristotle arrives at concerning each of them in the following table, giving references to the first lines of relevant passages in each invalid case [1].

TABLE 1

| | | LLL | LXL | XLL |
|---|---|---|---|---|
| First figure | Barbara | 1 Perfect | 15 Perfect | **29** Inv. by *red.* and ex. (30a23) |
| | Celarent | 2 Perfect | 16 Perfect | **30** Inv. Disproof as for 29 (30a32) |
| | Darii | 3 Perfect | 17 Perfect | **31** Inv. by lack of *red.* proof and ex. (30b2) |
| | Ferio | 4 Perfect | 18 Perfect | **32** Inv. by ex. (30b5) |
| Second figure | Cesare | 5 C. to 2 | 19 C. to 16 | **33** Inv. Disproof as for 20 |
| | Camestres | 6 C. to 2 | **20** Inv. by *red.* and ex. (30b18) | 34 C. to 16 |
| | Festino | 7 C. to 4 | 21 C. to 18 | **35** Inv. No disproof given |
| | Baroco | 8 Ecthesis | **22** Inv. by ex. (31a10) | **36** Inv. by ex. (31a15) |
| Third figure | Darapti | 9 C. to 3 | 23 C. to 17 | 37 C. to 17 |
| | Felapton | 10 C. to 4 | 24 C. to 18 | **38** Inv. by c. to 32 and ex. (31a37) |
| | Disamis | 11 C. to 3 | **25** Inv. by ex. (31b31) | 39 C. to 17 |
| | Datisi | 12 C. to 3 | 26 C. to 17 | **40** Inv. by c. to 31 and ex. (31b20) |
| | Bocardo | 13 Ecthesis | **27** Inv. by ex. (32a4) | **41** Inv. by ex. (31b40) |
| | Ferison | 14 C. to 4 | 28 C. to 18 | **42** Inv. by ex. (32a1) |

[1] Most of the information the table contains is to be found in Becker's table, ATM facing p. 25, and in Ross's table, facing p. 286, which this table is intended to supplement. Invalid syllogisms are in bold face, and "convert" is abbreviated to "C", "invalid" to "Inv.", "*reductio*" to "*red.*", and "example" to "ex.".

## 4. Aristotle on the two Barbaras

In the next seven sections, I wish to examine various attempts to provide an intuitive basis for accepting (or rejecting) Aristotle's views concerning the validity of the various moods presented above. I shall centre the discussion around the moods Barbara *LXL* and Barbara *XLL*, the difference in respect of validity of these two syllogisms being both crucial for our understanding of Aristotle's system and remarkable for the number of philosophers who have disputed it. I begin with Aristotle himself.

Barbara *LXL* must be taken as valid, Aristotle says, since if "*A* necessarily belongs to every *B*, and since *C* is one of the *B*'s, it is clear that for *C* also the positive ... relation to *A* will hold necessarily" (30a21–23). This argument does not seem to me conclusive: I do not see, for example, how Aristotle's restatement of the premisses will serve to show the invalidity of Barbara *XLL*.

More promising, at first sight, is Aristotle's suggestion (30b4) that from the denial of the conclusion of a valid syllogism there must result an impossibility, i.e. a proposition inconsistent with the premisses. What he is saying seems to be that any valid syllogism must be provable by a *reductio ad absurdum*. Let us try to prove in this way Barbara *LXL*:

| | |
|---|---|
| If | All *B* is necessarily *A* |
| and | All *C* is *B* |
| then | All *C* is necessarily *A*. |
| For suppose | Some *C* is not necessarily *A* |
| then, since | All *C* is *B* |
| it follows that | Some *B* is not necessarily *A*, which is absurd. |

This proof is appealing, but I do not think we should be satisfied with it. The *reductio* syllogism which it employs may be re-phrased as follows:

| | |
|---|---|
| If | Possibly some *C* is not *A* |
| and | All *C* is *B* |
| then | Possibly some *B* is not *A*, |

becoming Bocardo *MXM* in my notation, and this mood stands in need of validation just as much as Barbara *LXL*. Let those who find the logic of this *reductio* argument compelling consider a similar attempt to prove Barbara *XLL:*

| | |
|---|---|
| If | All *B* is *A* |
| and | All *C* is necessarily *B* |
| then | All *C* is necessarily *A*. |
| For suppose | Possibly some *C* is not *A* |
| then, since | All *B* is *A* |
| it follows that | Possibly some *C* is not *B*, which is absurd. |

Here the *reductio* syllogism, Baroco *XMM*, seems on the face of it just as valid or invalid as Bocardo *MXM*, and for this reason the method of proof by *reductio ad absurdum* cannot be used to distinguish between Barbaras *LXL* and *XLL*.

Ross discusses this *reductio* proof of Barbara *LXL* and finds it unconvincing. Not only that; he cannot believe Barbara *LXL* to be valid. Thus: "Aristotle's doctrine is plainly wrong. For what he is seeking to show is that the premisses prove not only that all *C* is *A*, but also that it is necessarily *A* just as all *B* is necessarily *A*, i.e. by a permanent necessity of its own nature; while what they do show is only that so long as all *C* is *B*, it is *A*, not by a permanent necessity of its own nature, but by a temporary necessity arising from its temporarily sharing in the nature of *B*" [1]. Ross also attacks the *reductio* syllogism Bocardo *MXM* in similar vein.

Łukasiewicz, commenting upon Ross's argument for rejecting Barbara *LXL*, seems unimpressed by it, although he confines himself to remarking that expressions like "permanent necessity of a thing's nature" belong to metaphysics, not to logic [2]. I think that Łukasiewicz is in the right here. Ross's view, when he speaks of the possibility of two terms being related by a "permanent necessity", implies that the two terms might be *in fact* so related, even though the word "necessarily" failed to occur in any proposition relating them. Alternatively, two terms might *in fact* fail to be so related, even though the word "necessarily" did occur in a proposition relating them. But in logic we cannot stop to consider such

[1] Ross, p. 43.
[2] Łukasiewicz, p. 186.

possibilities; we must deal with propositions *as they are stated in words*. Nothing more is accessible to us. And the only way we can determine the logical powers of a word like "necessarily" is to consider the validity or invalidity of arguments involving its use, such as Barbaras *LXL* and *XLL*.

Let us now return to Aristotle, and see if we can distinguish between the two Barbaras by pursuing a line of argument found in 30a23–28. The conclusion of Barbara *XLL* does not follow, Aristotle says. For suppose it did. We would have:

| | |
|---|---|
| If | All *B* is *A* |
| and | All *C* is necessarily *B* |
| then suppose | All *C* is necessarily *A*. |
| But | Some *B* is necessarily *C* (by conversion of the minor) |
| hence | Some *B* is necessarily *A* (by Darii *LLL*). |

But this last conclusion is according to Aristotle false, since the major premiss "All *B* is *A*" is quite compatible with its contradictory, namely "No *B* is necessarily *A*". This is an interesting argument which, although similar to a *reductio ad absurdum*, differs from the latter. In a *reductio* we assume the *falsehood* of the conclusion of an inference we wish to prove *valid:* here we assume the *truth* of the conclusion of an inference which we wish to prove *invalid*, and show that the consequences are such as to be more than what is strictly derivable from the original premisses. In this case, the original major premiss "All *B* is *A*" allows us to make no inference to either the truth or the falsehood of the proposition "No *B* is necessarily *A*" ("Possibly no *B* is *A*") [1]. Nor, presumably, will the addition of the original minor premiss make any difference; we are still not entitled to say any more than that the premisses are *consistent* with the proposition. But when we draw the conclusion of Barbara *XLL*, Darii *LLL* permits the deriving of a consequence of the original premisses which is *inconsistent* with "No *B* is necessarily *A*". Therefore we must reject Barbara *XLL*.

---

[1] Łukasiewicz would disagree here. See his p. 177, where from the truth of the proposition "R will see this at once" the author infers the falsehood of the proposition "It is possible that R will not see this at once".

It remains to show that the above argument does not invalidate Barbara *LXL*. This may be done by showing that the derivability of the latter's conclusion from its premisses entails no consequences which themselves contradict something consistent with these premisses. In fact, the conclusion of Barbara *LXL*,

All *C* is necessarily *A*,

when conjoined to the converse of the major premiss,

Some *A* is necessarily *B*,

yields no conclusion by any *LLL* or other syllogistic form of inference. Hence, Barbara *LXL* is not invalidated.

We conclude that Aristotle seems able satisfactorily to distinguish between the Barbaras in respect of their validity. However, his line of argument leads to some unsatisfactory results, as will be seen in the next section.

## 5. Hintikka's dilemma

Aristotle's *reductio*-type argument of 30a23–28, which, as was seen in the preceding section, enabled him to distinguish between the two Barbaras, has been challenged by Hintikka [1]. At least, what Hintikka shows is that the same sort of reasoning which Aristotle uses against the validity of Barbara *XLL* can be used against Darii *LXL*. Hintikka's argument (with slight modifications) runs as follows.

Take the valid mood Barbara *XLX*, which no one disputes (since we would get the same conclusion even if the second premiss were assertoric):

| | |
|---|---|
| If | All *B* is *A* |
| and | All *C* is necessarily *B* |
| then | All *C* is *A*, |

[1] J. Hintikka, *An Aristotelian Dilemma* [AD], Ajatus 22 (1959), pp. 87–92. This paper supplements the author's earlier *Necessity, Universality and Time in Aristotle*, Ajatus 20 (1957), pp. 65–90.

and convert its conclusion *per accidens:*

Some $A$ is $C$.

Then combine this with the minor premiss of Barbara $XLX$ to yield a conclusion by Darii $LXL$:

| | |
|---|---|
| If | All $C$ is necessarily $B$ |
| and | Some $A$ is $C$ |
| then | Some $A$ is necessarily $B$, |

which conclusion we convert to:

Some $B$ is necessarily $A$.

But *this* result is incompatible with the major premiss of Barbara $XLX$ in exactly the same way, according to Aristotle, as the conclusion of the combination of Barbara $XLL$ and Darii $LLL$ is incompatible with the major premiss of Barbara $XLL$. That is, the $B$'s of the major premiss of Barbara $XLX$ may be such that it is possible for no $B$ to be $A$, and *this* state of affairs is incompatible with "Some $B$ is necessarily $A$".

The steps by which we arrived at "Some $B$ is necessarily $A$" were as follows:

(1) Barbara $XLX$
(2) Conversion *per accidens* of "All $C$ is $A$"
(3) Darii $LXL$
(4) Simple conversion of "Some $A$ is necessarily $B$".

Of this chain of reasoning (1) and (2) are secure, and the weakest link seems to be (3). Against rejecting (4) we have Hintikka's opinion that "we should hesitate before rejecting any rule of conversion Aristotle uses. Since they are usually his most important tools, rejecting them would mean abandoning all hope of understanding what he actually had in mind in developing his syllogistic" [1]. Hence it seems that if we are to accept Aristotle's argument against the validity of Barbara $XLL$, we must accept it as also invalidating Darii $LXL$.

---

[1] Hintikka, AD p. 91.

However, I do not think we should make more of Hintikka's objections than is warranted. Hintikka says (AD p. 87) that, in some cases where he rejects an apodeictic conclusion for a mixed mood, Aristotle rejects "those and only those apodeictic conclusions that would in turn yield, together with the apodeictic premiss, an apodeictic conclusion concerning the terms occurring in the assertoric premiss". In the case of Barbara *XLL*, the conclusion cannot be validly drawn, since "All *B* is *A*" must be compatible with "Possibly no *B* is *A*". But this line of argument cannot be used to show why Darii *XLL* is invalid, nor can it be used directly against Darii *LXL*, since in both cases the conclusion, when combined with the apodeictic premiss, yields nothing. Hence even Aristotle must have had *other* criteria of validity and invalidity, and we may therefore hope to escape Hintikka's dilemma.

To sum up, though Hintikka has shown that in producing his argument against Barbara *XLL* Aristotle has also inadvertently provided a means of invalidating Darii *LXL*, we should not conclude that the two must inevitably stand or fall together. It will in fact be the task of sections 9 and 10 to provide a way of separating them.

## 6. Theophrastus and Łukasiewicz on the two Barbaras

Theophrastus and Łukasiewicz differ both from Aristotle and from each other on the validity of the two Barbaras, Theophrastus holding them to be both invalid, and Łukasiewicz both valid. Their reasons for doing so, however, are less different than might be expected.

Alexander tells us that Theophrastus upheld the "*peiorem*" rule for modal syllogisms, maintaining that the conclusion followed the weaker premiss (*peiorem semper sequitur conclusio partem*). The order of strength was: necessary, assertoric, possible; so that, for example, syllogisms containing an assertoric premiss could never be supplied with a necessary conclusion.

This principle plainly rules out Barbara *LXL* as a valid mood. Arguing for its invalidity, Theophrastus proceeds as follows: Since the minor premiss is not necessary, the bond between the two terms will not be necessary either, and the minor term will hence be "separable" from the middle. But if this is so, then the minor will also be "separable" from the other extreme, the major, even though the major and the middle are necessarily joined [1]. What is being appealed to in this notion of "separability" is a *spatial* analogy. Theophrastus makes use of similar appeals to our spatial imagination on two other occasions, causing Bochenski to describe the idea of spatial form as "une des idées maîtresses du système théophrastien".

Another appeal to our spatial imagination is made by Łukasiewicz, but with the opposite aim at proving the *validity*, not only of Barbara *LXL*, but also of Barbara *XLL*. Let us suppose, he says, that the expression "All *C* is necessarily *B*" (the minor of Barbara *XLL*) means "Every *C* is connected by a wire with a *B*". Since every *B* is an *A* (the major of Barbara *XLL*), it is evident that every *C* will also be connected by a wire with an *A* (the conclusion of Barbara *XLL*) [2].

What are we to say here? Two equally compelling arguments, based on spatial analogy, lead to opposite conclusions. Theophrastus concentrates on the *weakness* of the *assertoric* premisses of the Barbaras, which leads him to assert the weakness of the conclusion, while Łukasiewicz concentrates on the *strength* of the *necessary* premisses, leading to the strength of the conclusion. Aristotle, on the other hand, seems to concentrate on neither: his system escapes the net of spatial analogy entirely.

## 7. Concrete examples of the two Barbaras

So far we have considered Barbaras *LXL* and *XLL* only in their abstract form, with letters for terms. However, as remarked earlier, when Aristotle tries to disprove Barbara *XLL*, he gives an example of it with concrete terms. But Theophrastus was also able to give examples with concrete terms designed to disprove Barbara *LXL*.

---

[1] See Bochenski, LT, pp. 79–80. Also the translation of Alexander's text in Ross, p. 41: "If *B* belongs to all *C*, but not of necessity, the two may be disjoined, and when *B* is disjoined from *C*, *A* also will be disjoined from it".

[2] Adapted from Łukasiewicz, p. 186.

Thus in his opinion the syllogism

| | |
|---|---|
| If | All that walks is necessarily in movement |
| and | All men are walking |
| then | All men are necessarily in movement [1], |

might very well have both its premisses true (i.e. at a time when all men *were* walking), but not its conclusion. Barbara *LXL* would hence be invalid [2].

Defenders of Aristotle have pointed out that Theophrastus' examples are unfair. They are unfair in that they introduce premisses κατὰ χρόνον, with temporal reference, while Aristotle explicitly restricts assertoric premisses to stating something permanently true of a class. Thus "we must understand 'that which belongs to all' with no limitation in respect of time, e.g. to the present or to a particular period, but simply without qualification. For it is by the help of such premisses that we make syllogisms, since if the premiss is understood with reference to the present moment, there cannot be a syllogism" (34b7–11). In Theophrastus' example the minor premiss does indeed refer to the present moment, and hence his criticism seems to miss its mark.

Unfortunately, though, the example that Aristotle gives to disprove Barbara *XLL* also makes use of a premiss κατὰ χρόνον, the premiss "all animals are in movement". And if we restrict ourselves to premisses that are timelessly true (which it seems Aristotle does not: see as additional instances his concrete examples disproving Ferio *XLL* and Datisi *XLL*), then we get not only examples

---

[1] This example is one of three found in Alexander. See Ross, p. 42.

[2] There is an interesting attempt made by Averroes to nullify Theophrastus' counter-example by defending the necessity of the conclusion. All men *are* necessarily in movement, Averroes says; not insofar as they are men, but insofar as they are walking. "*Et deceptio in hoc* (i.e. in Theophrastus' example) *est, quoniam ambulans non movetur ex necessitate, ex parte qua est homo, sed ex parte qua est ambulans . . . Puta, ex necessitate, omnis homo movetur, ex parte qua est ambulans*". (*Media Expositio in Libros Priorum Resolutoriorum, lib.* I *cap.* 10, tr. Joannes Franciscus Burana, Venice 1562, *fol.* 28v.)

such as this for Barbara *LXL:*

| | |
|---|---|
| If | All men are necessarily rational |
| and | All Greeks are men |
| then | All Greeks are necessarily rational, |

but also seemingly equally valid examples such as this for Barbara *XLL:*

| | |
|---|---|
| If | All vertebrates are animals |
| and | All men are necessarily vertebrates |
| then | All men are necessarily animals. |

Hence it seems that whether or not we rule out Theophrastus' (and Aristotle's) examples κατὰ χρόνον, we shall not be able to use such examples to distinguish between the two Barbaras.

Before leaving Theophrastus' counter-examples, we may ask whether they prove anything at all. I think that they do prove something, namely that in Aristotle's modal syllogistic the word "necessarily" cannot be taken to mean either "by definition", or "it is analytic that", or "it is true by the meanings of the words alone that". That is to say, if one asserts that *by definition* everything that walks moves, this is not equivalent to asserting that *necessarily* everything that walks moves; at least, not in Aristotle's sense of the word "necessarily". Theophrastus' examples show this. For while one might agree that by definition everything that walks moves, one could not agree that by definition every man was in movement. If Aristotle wishes to maintain the validity of the syllogistic form of which Theophrastus' examples are concrete instances, he cannot take "necessarily" to mean "by definition". Similarly for the other proposed meanings.

## 8. The Becker approach and its congeners

Bochenski states that Aristotle's modal syllogistic, though "well-known and developed during the Middle Ages, was later almost completely misunderstood until A. Becker rediscovered its true meaning" [1]. Certainly Becker did much to render the theory in-

---

[1] *Ancient Formal Logic*, Amsterdam 1951, p. 55.

telligible. But there are serious difficulties about his interpretation.

Becker bases his theory of the modal moods upon a certain understanding of the "structure" of modal premisses. All "structuralist" interpretations of Aristotle take as their text the following passage:

"The expression 'it is possible for this to belong to that' may be understood in two senses: either as 'to the thing to which that belongs' or as 'to the thing to which that can belong' "[1].

Here it appears that Aristotle is saying that the proposition "It is possible for $B$ to belong to all $A$" may be understood in two senses, namely:

(1) All that is $A$ is possibly $B$,
or (2) All that is possibly $A$ is possibly $B$.

Becker proposes the following quantified forms as giving the precise meaning of these two senses:

(1) $(x)(Ax \supset E_2Bx)$
and (2) $(x)(E_2Ax \supset E_2Bx)$[2].

He makes use of both these interpretations in setting forth and formalizing Aristotle's system of moods with contingent premisses: for moods with one contingent and one assertoric premiss he uses (1), and for moods with two contingent premisses he uses (1) for one premiss and (2) for the other, while noting that Aristotle never says in which cases he wishes the second interpretation to be used. We get the impression, from Becker's treatment, that Aristotle suspected that the proposition "All $A$ is possibly $B$" was ambiguous, but was unclear in his own mind which of its different possible interpretations he was employing at any one time.

The situation is somewhat similar in the case of the apodeictic moods. In moods with one necessary and one assertoric premiss, Becker says, Aristotle interprets "All $A$ is necessarily $B$" as follows:

(3) $(x)(Ax \supset \Box Bx)$[3]

---

[1] 32b25–29 in Bochenski's translation, HFL p. 83.

[2] Becker, ATM, p. 33. The symbol $E_2$ is used by Becker to denote "two-sided possibility", or contingency, for a discussion of which see sect. 22.

[3] Becker, ATM, p. 39. For quantified forms I drop the Polish notation and revert to "$\Box$" for necessity and "$\Diamond$" for (one-sided) possibility.

Barbara *LXL* then becomes:

If $(x)(Bx \supset \Box Cx)$
and $(x)(Ax \supset Bx)$
then $(x)(Ax \supset \Box Cx)$

while Barbara *XLL* is of the invalid form:

If $(x)(Bx \supset Cx)$
and $(x)(Ax \supset \Box Bx)$
then $(x)(Ax \supset \Box Cx)$

Using interpretation (3), then, Becker can satisfactorily distinguish between the two Barbaras. The trouble comes when we wish to convert apodeictic premisses; in order, for example, to derive Cesare *LXL* from Celarent *LXL*. The major premiss of the latter is

$$(x)(Bx \supset \Box \sim Cx) \quad (4)$$

while that of Cesare *LXL* is

$$(x)(Cx \supset \Box \sim Bx) \quad (5)$$

and no known logical operation will lead us from (4) to (5). Becker's solution to this problem is to say, once again, that Aristotle's conception of his own apodeictic premisses is ambiguous, and that his rules of conversion require the modal operator to stand at the beginning of the proposition. (4) would then become:

$$\Box (x)(Bx \supset \sim Cx) \quad (6)$$

which is convertible into the new analogue of (5), namely

$$\Box (x)(Cx \supset \sim Bx) \quad (7)$$

by use of the formula $(p \supset q) \supset (\Box p \supset \Box q)$ [1].

Aristotle, according to Becker, did not recognize the ambiguous character of his modal premisses, although Becker conjectures that, with increasing familiarity with the subject, he would eventually have noticed it. As it is, Aristotle's work contains a "logical inconsistency" [2]. There is, however, another way of looking at the

---

[1] Becker, ATM, p. 42.

[2] Becker, ATM, p. 64. The ambiguity bears an obvious resemblance to the difference between modal propositions *de dicto* and *de re*.

matter. If Aristotle's system is ambiguous and/or inconsistent under the Becker interpretation, and if another interpretation can be found which restores its consistency and coherence, then so much the worse for the Becker interpretation. Before we examine the possibilities of a new interpretation, though, we should see exactly where each of the different Becker-type interpretations breaks down.

I say "Becker-type interpretations", because there are many possible such interpretations. Von Wright [1] uses Becker's (6) above, Sugihara [2] lists five alternatives, and Rescher [3] six. Restricting ourselves to apodeictic universal and particular affirmative premisses alone, Becker's alternatives are (i) and (ii) below, von Wright's is (ii), Sugihara's are (i)–(v), and Rescher's (i)–(iv) and (vi)–(vii).

| | *Universal* | *Particular* |
|---|---|---|
| (i) | $(x)(Ax \supset \Box Bx)$ | $(\exists x)(Ax \cdot \Box Bx)$ |
| (ii) | $\Box (x)(Ax \supset Bx)$ | $\Box (\exists x)(Ax \cdot Bx)$ |
| (iii) | $(x) \Box (Ax \supset Bx)$ | $(\exists x) \Box (Ax \cdot Bx)$ |
| (iv) | $(x)(\Box Ax \supset \Box Bx)$ | $(\exists x)(\Box Ax \cdot \Box Bx)$ |
| (v) | $(x)(\Diamond Ax \supset \Box Bx)$ | $(\exists x)(\Box Ax \cdot \Box Bx)$ |
| (vi) | $(x)(\Diamond Ax \supset Bx)$ | $(\exists x)(\Box Ax \cdot Bx)$ |
| (vii) | $(x)(\Box Ax \supset Bx)$ | $(\exists x)(\Box Ax \cdot Bx)$ |

None of these interpretations does justice to Aristotle's system. Not one of them even simultaneously provides for the validity of Barbaras *LLL* and *LXL*, the invalidity of Barbara *XLL*, and the convertibility of the particular premiss "Some *A* is necessarily *B*" into "Some *B* is necessarily *A*". We have in fact the following results to compare with Aristotle's, where "V" and "I" denote "valid" and "invalid" respectively [4].

---

[1] *An Essay in Modal Logic*, Amsterdam 1951, Appendix I.

[2] *Necessity and Possibility in Aristotelian Syllogistic*, Memoirs of the Liberal Arts College, Fukui University, 6 (1957), pp. 75–87, and 7 (1957), pp. 15–22.

[3] Rescher, sect. VI.

[4] In the derivation of these results the following propositional theses, to be found in Lewis's S3–S5, were used: $\Box p \prec p$, $\Box (p . q) = (\Box p . \Box q)$, and $(p \prec q) \prec (\Box p \prec \Box q)$.

TABLE 2

| | Aristotle | (i) | (ii) | (iii) | (iv) | (v) | (vi) | (vii) |
|---|---|---|---|---|---|---|---|---|
| Barbara *LLL* | V | V | V | V | V | V | V | I |
| Barbara *LXL* | V | V | I | I | I | I | I | I |
| Barbara *XLL* | I | I | I | I | I | I | V | V |
| Conversion of particular premiss | V | I | V | V | V | V | I | I |

We conclude that no Becker-type interpretation of Aristotle's modal premisses is satisfactory.

## 9. Rescher's interpretation

Reflection on the failings of both the Becker and the Łukasiewicz approach has led Rescher to despair of finding *any* formal interpretation of Aristotle's system. Instead he offers a non-formal interpretation, urging us to look to the *Posterior Analytics* for guidance as to what is being attempted in the *Prior Analytics.* In the former, which treats of demonstration rather than of inference from (possibly false) premisses, we read that "demonstration is an inference from necessary premisses" (73a24), and that "demonstrative knowledge must be knowledge of a necessary nexus, and therefore must clearly be obtained through a necessary middle term; otherwise its possessor will know neither the cause nor the fact that his conclusion is a necessary connexion" (75a12–15). It fairly strikes one that here Aristotle must be referring to the apodeictic syllogism.

To the apodeictic syllogism, yes, but if so only to the *LLL* syllogism, for in *An. post.* Aristotle explicitly says that if the conclusion is to be necessary, both premisses must be [1]. The problem of whether *An. pr.* is earlier or later than *An. post.* is discussed in a masterful way by Ross [2], though it is remarkable that in the discussion he nowhere mentions the striking fact that in *An. post. LXL* syllogisms are passed over in favour of *LLL* ones.

---

[1] Cf. 87b22–25: "All reasoning proceeds from necessary or general premisses, the conclusion being necessary if the premisses are necessary and general if the premisses are general".

[2] Ross, pp. 6–23.

Still, our problem is independent of this one. It may be possible to give a justification for the mixed moods of *An. pr.* whether Aristotle later abandoned them or not, and this is what Rescher tries to do. He says: "The view of scientific reasoning underlying the discussion of apodeictic syllogisms in *An. pr.* seems to be that (1) the major premiss lays down a necessary rule of some sort, (2) the minor describes some special case which has been shown by observation or induction to fall under this rule, so that (3) the conclusion is justified that this special case necessarily conforms to the rule. The paradigm of such reasoning is:

"Law (necessary rule): All $B$'s are $A$'s (All twinkling things are distant)

Special Case (observation): All $C$'s are $B$'s (All stars are twinkling things)

Explained Consequence (necessary result): All $C$'s are $A$'s (All stars are distant)" [1].

This attempt of Rescher's to explain the validity of Barbara *LXL*, where the minor is a "special case" of the necessary rule of the major, can also be extended to explain the invalidity of Barbara *XLL* by stipulating that the latter's major cannot be a "special case" of the minor at all. Nor is this stipulation far-fetched. In the first figure the terms can be viewed as overlapping each other in the following way:

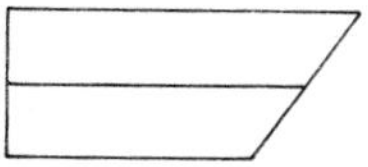

major
middle
minor
related by major premiss
related by minor premiss

so that the first step in Rescher's interpretation, namely

major premiss : minor premiss : : general rule : special case

seems justified. In fact this step is strongly reminiscent of the

[1] Rescher, sect. IX.

*dictum de omni*. But there is a difference, and this is the second step. In Rescher's interpretation the modality of the conclusion can be upgraded above that of the minor premiss, and there is nothing analogous to this upgrading in the *dictum de omni*. Hence he lays it down, again in the first figure, that where the modality of the major premiss is stronger [1] than that of the minor, the modality of the conclusion is also stronger than that of the minor. In cases where the modality of the major is not stronger than that of the minor, the modality of the conclusion simply follows that of the major.

Rescher's rules for upgrading may seem to have an *ad hoc* air. But the *ad hoc*-ness vanishes if we combine steps one and two in his interpretation and note that the upgrading occurs *in just those instances* where one premiss is a "special case" of the other. Thus for mixed necessary/assertoric moods we may lay it down that, when one premiss is a "special case" of the other, the latter being the "general rule", the modality of the conclusion follows that of the general rule. If the general rule is necessary, the conclusion is necessary; if not, not. Himself implicitly combining the two steps in his interpretation, Rescher states that "a rule that is necessarily (say) applicable to all of a group, will be necessarily applicable to any subgroup, pretty much regardless of how this subgroup is constituted ... If all elms are necessarily deciduous, and all trees in my yard are elms, then all trees in my yard are necessarily deciduous (even if it is not necessary that the trees in my yard be elms)" [2].

The upshot of this is, that we can give an intuitive justification for the upgrading of the conclusions of moods like Barbara *LXL*, and for the non-upgrading of those of moods like Barbara *XLL*, if we can give a satisfactory account of what it is for one premiss to be a "special case" of the other. This will be the task of the next section.

---

[1] I.e. higher in the scale necessary-assertoric-possible-contingent. Rescher's interpretation is so phrased as to apply to the other mixed moods discussed by Aristotle in addition to the necessary/assertoric.

[2] Rescher, sect. IX.

## 10. Completion of Rescher's interpretation

In the case of the first figure only is it plausible to say that the minor premiss is always a "special case" of the major. In the second and third figures, there cannot be any such pat formula as this, for the pairs Cesare *LXL* and Camestres *XLL*, Datisi *LXL* and Disamis *XLL*, indicate that the minor can be at one time the "special case" of the major, at another time its "general rule". If we wish to uphold the principle that the modality of the conclusion follows that of the general rule, we must have a way of determining, in all cases, which premiss *is* the general rule. Nor will it do to say that all second and third figure moods containing supposed instances of general rules must be reducible to the first figure by the laws of conversion of necessary premisses, for these laws themselves require intuitive justification. This is especially true of conversion *per accidens:* it is not obvious why "All men are necessarily rational" implies "Some rational beings are necessarily men". No, a criterion of "general rule" and "special case" is needed which is applicable to all figures independently of conversion.

Such a criterion may be provided by reviving the traditional doctrine of distribution. One way of stating this rather confusing doctrine is to say that a term in a premiss is distributed if it *actually* denotes or refers to, in that premiss, the whole of the class of entities which it is *capable* of denoting. Another, clearer, way is to say that

| | | |
|---|---|---|
| in the premiss | All *A* is *B*, | *A* is distributed, *B* undistributed |
| ,, ,, ,, | No *A* is *B*, | *A* and *B* are distributed |
| ,, ,, ,, | Some *A* is *B*, | *A* and *B* are undistributed |
| ,, ,, ,, | Some *A* is not *B*, | *A* is undistributed, *B* distributed. |

For our criterion, we focus attention upon the middle term, which in any valid syllogism must be distributed at least once. We say, with two restrictions noted below, that a premiss in which the middle term is distributed serves as the *general rule* of which the other premiss is a *special case.* This criterion accords well with reason, for it is natural that of the two premisses sharing the middle term, that one should be more general whose middle term refers to the whole of its own denotation. If the middle term is distributed in both premisses, then either can serve, in turn, as the special case of the other. This happens in the case of Darapti, the double distribution of whose middle term is reflected in the validity of both Darapti *LXL* and *XLL*.

Now for the restrictions. In Baroco, the middle term is distributed in the minor premiss, yet Baroco *XLL* is not held to be valid by Aristotle. To accord with Aristotle's system, we therefore impose the restriction that (a) a universal premiss cannot be the "special case" of a particular premiss. Again, in Felapton and Bocardo, the middle term is distributed in the minor premiss, but Aristotle does not admit Felapton *XLL* or Bocardo *XLL*. Hence we stipulate that (b) a negative premiss cannot be the "special case" of an affirmative premiss. The following table shows the distribution of the middle term in the various moods, and indicates the mixture of necessary and assertoric premisses which yields a necessary conclusion. The invalid moods which require restrictions (a) and (b) to rule them out are placed in brackets. "***b***" indicates that *b* is distributed.

TABLE 3

| *Mood* | *Premisses* | | *Conclusion* | *Modality* | |
|---|---|---|---|---|---|
| Barbara | *A***b***c* | *Aab* | *Aac* | *LXL* | |
| Celarent | *E***b***c* | *Aab* | *Eac* | *LXL* | |
| Darii | *A***b***c* | *Iab* | *Iac* | *LXL* | |
| Ferio | *E***b***c* | *Iab* | *Oac* | *LXL* | |
| Cesare | *Ec***b** | *Aab* | *Eac* | *LXL* | |
| Camestres | *Acb* | *Ea***b** | *Eac* | | *XLL* |
| Festino | *Ec***b** | *Iab* | *Oac* | *LXL* | |
| Baroco | *Acb* | *Oa***b** | *Oac* | | (*XLL*) |
| Darapti | *A***b***c* | *A***b***a* | *Iac* | *LXL* | *XLL* |
| Felapton | *E***b***c* | *A***b***a* | *Oac* | *LXL* | (*XLL*) |
| Disamis | *Ibc* | *A***b***a* | *Iac* | | *XLL* |
| Datisi | *A***b***c* | *Iba* | *Iac* | *LXL* | |
| Bocardo | *Obc* | *A***b***a* | *Oac* | | (*XLL*) |
| Ferison | *E***b***c* | *Iba* | *Oac* | *LXL* | |

In order to test the accuracy of the interpretation, table 3 should be compared with table 1, page 9.

To recapitulate, we have presented an intuitive justification of the validity of Aristotle's mixed necessary/assertoric moods by (i) dividing the premisses of such moods into "general rule" and "special case", and (ii) allowing the modality of the conclusion to follow that of the "general rule". In order to decide which of the two premisses is the "general rule", and which the "special case", the notion of distribution is appealed to, it being laid down (iii) that any premiss in which the middle term is distributed can serve as the "general rule" of which the other premiss is a "special case". Finally, two restrictions on (iii) are necessary, namely (a) a universal premiss cannot be the "special case" of a particular premiss, and (b) a negative premiss cannot be the "special case" of an affirmative premiss.

CHAPTER II

# THE SYSTEM OF APODEICTIC MOODS

## 11. Systematization of the assertoric moods

Preparatory to axiomatizing Aristotle's system of apodeictic moods, we shall briefly consider the work of his followers in completing and systematizing the assertoric moods. Aristotle did not recognize the fourth figure as distinct from the other three, but he was perfectly aware of the existence of the five valid fourth-figure moods: Bramantip, Camenes, Dimaris, Fresison and Fesapo. These he treated not as independent moods, but as auxiliary to the first figure [1]. There is doubt as to which logician first explicitly separated the fourth from the other three figures, but there can be none as to the validity of the moods of that figure themselves, given the validity of the rules of conversion by which they may be reduced to other valid moods. The same is true of the "subaltern" moods with weakened conclusion: Barbari, Celaront, Cesaro, Camestrop and Camenop. Despite the low esteem in which they were traditionally held (thus we find in Aldrich that "*nomen habent nullum, nec, si bene colligis, usum*" [2]), their validity follows inexorably from those laws of the square of opposition known as the laws of subalternation (e.g. "All $A$ is $B$" implies "Some $A$ is $B$").

These 10 fourth-figure and subaltern moods swell the total number of assertoric moods to 24, and the system, thus completed, exhibits

---

[1] See *An. pr.* 53a3–12 for Bramantip, Camenes and Dimaris, 29a19–26 for Fresison and Fesapo, and Ross p. 35 for comments.

[2] Aldrich, *Artis Logicae Rudimenta,* ed. Mansel, Oxford 1849, p. 72. Actually, the names of the subaltern moods are found in Peter of Mantua (Bochenski, HFL, p. 215) and the moods themselves in Ariston the Alexandrian (HFL, p. 140).

some elegant interrelationships. Each mood, by *reductio ad absurdum* arguments interchanging the contradictory of the conclusion with the contradictory of the major and minor premiss in turn, is seen to be equivalent to two other moods. It is in this way, for example, that Aristotle proves Baroco and Bocardo *XXX* from Barbara *XXX;* similarly from Celarent we may derive Festino and Disamis [1]. Again, Celarent and Cesare are seen to be equivalent to one another through the mutual convertibility of their majors, and the validity of Datisi implies the validity of Darapti by virtue of the one-way relation of subalternation between their minors. These relations of equivalence and implication among the 24 moods make for a compact and unified system. In the following table, the three moods each reducible to one another by *reductio ad absurdum* are written in a column, those moods derivable from one another by the simple conversion of premisses or conclusion are joined by "↔", and those implied by another mood through subalternation of premiss or conclusion are joined to it by "→":

TABLE 4

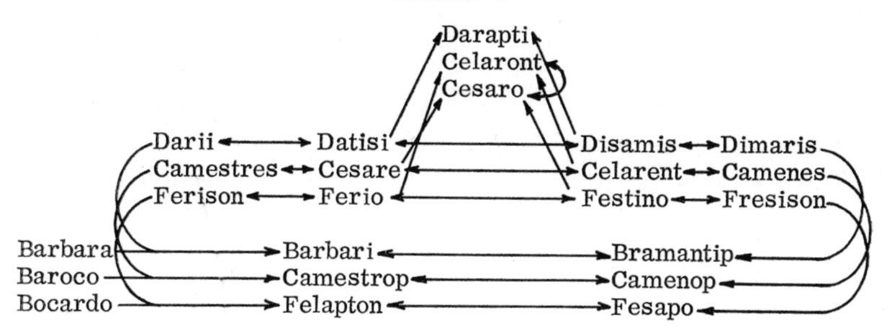


Once the system is exhibited in this way, there seems little reason for not accepting the fourth figure and subaltern moods as an integral part of it. It is interesting to note, though, that the first three figures are much more closely intermingled than the fourth, which is relatively isolated in two distinct groups.

It was Łukasiewicz who brought the assertoric moods into the 20th century by axiomatizing them in a formal system complete

---

[1] This way in which the moods fall into groups of three was known to Leibniz. See L. Couturat, *La logique de Leibniz*, Paris 1901, p. 14.

with rejection and decision procedure [1]. Łukasiewicz is able to derive all 24 valid moods, plus the laws of conversion and subalternation, from the following four axioms:

1. *Aaa*
2. *Iaa*
3. *CK Abc Aab Aac* (Barbara)
4. *CK Abc Iba Iac* (Datisi)

Słupecki has shown that Łukasiewicz's system provides a complete theory of the relations of inclusion and intersection of non-null classes [2], so that Aristotle's system may be said to have found its permanent place in the modern logic of classes.

It is notorious that not all the relations of Aristotle's system hold true if we admit empty classes as values of the variables *a*, *b*, *c*, etc. In particular, the relation of subalternation *C Aab Iab* does not hold. The system from which this relation is excluded is the one containing those moods which satisfy the Venn diagramatic test, namely the twelve central moods of table 4 plus Barbara, Baroco and Bocardo. This system can be axiomatized by omitting the axiom *Iaa* from Łukasiewicz's set. A glance at table 4 tells us that other such sub-systems are possible. The smallest of these, permitting of *reductio* proofs and containing all the laws of conversion and of the square of opposition, is that consisting only of the three moods at the top of table 4: it may be axiomatized by Darapti plus *Aaa* plus the law of conversion *C Iab Iba*.

## 12. Modal logic of propositions

As was seen above, it is the laws of conversion and of the square of opposition which provide the means by which we may derive one valid assertoric mood from another. Similarly it will be the laws of a modal square of opposition which will enable us to systematize the modal moods. Before constructing such a square, however,

---

[1] Though see an earlier, not completely formalized, axiomatization of syllogistic with negative terms in Prof. J. W. Miller's *The Structure of Aristotelian Logic*, London, 1938.

[2] This result is referred to in J. C. Shepherdson, *On the Interpretation of Aristotelian Syllogistic*, The Journal of Symbolic Logic, 21 (1956) p. 137.

we must investigate certain laws belonging to the modal logic of unanalysed propositions.

A preliminary discussion of the opposition of modal propositions is to be found in the 12th and 13th books of Aristotle's *De interpretatione*, an earlier work than the *Prior Analytics*. Aristotle is there concerned to discover, among other things, the contradictory of a given modal proposition. His first discovery is that "it may not be" (*MNp*) is not the contradictory of "it may be" (*Mp*); for, he points out, both these propositions may be true of the same subject – a cloak may be cut and it may not be cut. Similarly, the contradictory of "it is necessary that it should be" (*Lp*) is not "it is necessary that it should not be" (*LNp*), but "it is not necessary that it should be" (*NLp*) (22a3). Finally, in 22b24–27 the proposition "it is not necessary that it should not be" (*NLNp*) is taken as the contradictory of the proposition "it is impossible that it should be" (*NMp*), from which it would appear that Aristotle regarded "it is not necessary that it should not be" (*NLNp*) and "it is possible that it should be" (*Mp*) as equivalents.

The equivalence *EMpNLNp* is one of those formulae belonging to what Łukasiewicz calls "basic modal logic". As we shall see, Aristotle makes use of this equivalence in constructing *reductio* arguments. Of the other formulae asserted in "basic modal logic", *CLpp* and *CpMp*, Aristotle makes less use. He *could* have made considerable use of them; for example from *CLpp* and Barbara *LXL* it is a simple matter to derive the mood Barbara *LXX*, but this mood is not mentioned by Aristotle. Still less does he appeal to the modal "laws of extensionality" [1], which go beyond basic modal logic and which Łukasiewicz claims Aristotle recognized and accepted – more, one feels, because Łukasiewicz's own systematization of the modal moods required them than because Aristotle's did. The "*L*-law of extensionality", which is said to be stated by Aristotle in 34a22–24, has the form *CCpqCLpLq*, and with its help Łukasiewicz is able to prove both Barbaras *LXL* and *XLL* from Barbara *XXX* [2]. In a similar manner it is possible to prove

---

[1] Łukasiewicz, p. 138.

[2] Łukasiewicz, p. 189.

an *LXL* and an *XLL* mood from every valid *XXX* mood, and so to destroy the "fragmentary" nature of the apodeictic syllogistic by filling up all the invalid gaps of table 1.

It is my opinion that the "fragmentary" nature of Aristotle's modal syllogistic is one of its chief points of interest. If this be so, then no reconstruction of his system which does not preserve its fragmentation will be of much value. Łukasiewicz's is one of such reconstructions. Hence, if we are to be true to Aristotle, we must forego the use of the *L*-law of extensionality.

As a matter of fact it is doubtful whether Aristotle does state the *L*-law of extensionality in 34a22–24. He says there that if we indicate the premisses of a syllogism by *A*, and the conclusion by *B*, then if *A* is necessary *B* is necessary. This would seem to justify only the inferring of *LLL* syllogistic moods from *XXX* moods; not, as the law of extensionality states, a proposition *CLpLq* from a proposition *Cpq*. But in any case, I think we should try to avoid basing any proofs in modal syllogistic on laws belonging to the modal logic of propositions – even the laws *CLpp* and *CpMp*. For either these laws are not sufficiently sensitive, as is the case with the *L*-law of extensionality, to make those fine discriminations between validity and invalidity which Aristotle's system demands, or in them unrestricted substitution for variables cannot be allowed, as is the case with *CLpp*. Aristotle gives us absolutely no clue as to how we should interpret the iterated modality *LMAab* in the expression *C LMAab MAab*, although the latter is a substitution of *CLpp* and would have to be accepted as a thesis of our modal system if *CLpp* were incorporated into what Łukasiewicz calls its "auxiliary theory", i.e. the propositional logic underlying it. Even if we took Lewis's modal system S5 as our auxiliary theory, so that iterated modalities were reducible to simple ones, we would still be faced with problematic formulae such as *C Abc LC Aab Aac*. Though the latter is well-formed, we have no basis for deciding whether Aristotle would have considered it true or false. Hence we shall accept into our auxiliary theory no theses not belonging to unmodalized propositional logic, with the exception of *EMpNLNp*, which we shall in fact treat as a definition of *M*.

I shall have more to say about the modal logic of propositions in sect. 22, when we come to consider the distinction Aristotle makes between possibility (τὸ δυνατόν and τὸ ἐνδεχόμενον in the weak sense) and two-sided possibility or contingency (τὸ ἐνδεχόμενον in the strong sense). In the present chapter I shall be treating of possibility in the first of these senses only.

## 13. Opposition of modal premisses

Throughout the *De interpretatione* Aristotle considers only the opposition of propositions formed by applying modal operators to propositions not further analysed into terms and expressions showing quantity. That is, he is concerned only with finding the contradictory of propositions like "it is necessary that $p$" rather than of propositions like "it is necessary that all $A$ is $B$". The various relations of contradiction and implication holding among these latter propositions, which occur as premisses in modal syllogisms, are not discussed directly by Aristotle. We may, however, gather from the *Prior Analytics* what his laws of opposition for modal premisses would be.

Let us begin, not with Aristotle, but with a survey of what our collective intuition, as expressed in the English language, can tell us. For example, if we assert that

1. Necessarily all $A$ is $B$,

then we cannot also hold that the following is true:

2. Possibly some $A$ is not $B$.

Similarly if 2 is true, 1 cannot be true. Again, if we deny 1, it seems intuitively that we must uphold the truth of 2, and if 2 is denied, 1 must be asserted. In short, we say that 1 and 2 are contradictories. That the following pairs are also contradictories may be seen in the same way:

3. Necessarily some $A$ is $B$

and 4. Possibly no $A$ is $B$;

5. Necessarily no $A$ is $B$

and 6. Possibly some $A$ is $B$;

7. Necessarily some $A$ is not $B$

and 8. Possibly all $A$ is $B$.

These results may be obtained in a purely formal manner, without the aid of intuition, through the use of the equivalence of "possibly" and "not necessarily not" referred to in sect. 12. Negating 1 we obtain "It is not the case that necessarily all $A$ is $B$", which is "Possibly it is not the case that all $A$ is $B$', or "Possibly some $A$ is not $B$". Nor does it matter to the sense of these modal premisses whether we write them in their *de dicto* or *de re* forms, i.e. whether we write "Necessarily all $A$ is $B$" or "All $A$ is necessarily $B$". Care is called for in the case of negative propositions, however, since the *de re* equivalent of "Possibly some $A$ is not $B$" is not "Some $A$ is not possibly $B$", but "Some $A$ is possibly not $B$", i.e. "Some $A$ is not necessarily $B$". Again, "Necessarily no $A$ is $B$", is equivalent not to "No $A$ is necessarily $B$", but to "It is not the case that possibly some $A$ is $B$", i.e. to "It is not the case that some $A$ is possibly $B$", i.e. "No $A$ is possibly $B$".

Viewed in this light, one argument for regarding the Schoolmen's distinction between modalities *de dicto* and *de re* as one of content as well as of form evaporates. Admittedly the *de dicto* "Necessarily no $A$ is $B$" is not the same as the *de re* "No $A$ is necessarily $B$". But this is merely because the *de re* form has been incorrectly constructed out of the *de dicto* form. There is no difference in meaning between "Necessarily no $A$ is $B$" and "No $A$ is possibly $B$".

It should be noted that the modal words "must" and "may" generally follow the *de re* rather than the *de dicto* applications of "necessarily" and "possibly" respectively. Thus, "Necessarily some $A$ is $B$" is the same as "Some $A$ must be $B$", but its contradictory "Possibly no $A$ is $B$", whose *de re* form is "No $A$ is necessarily $B$" is equivalent to "No $A$ must be $B$". All these relations of equivalence and of contradiction appear in the following table, where groups of mutual equivalents are joined by straight lines to their contradictories:

TABLE 5

| | |
|---|---|
| Necessarily all $A$ is $B$<br>All $A$ is necessarily $B$<br>All $A$ must be $B$ | Necessarily no $A$ is $B$<br>No $A$ is possibly $B$<br>No $A$ may be $B$ |
| Necessarily some $A$ is $B$<br>Some $A$ is necessarily $B$<br>Some $A$ must be $B$ | Necessarily some $A$ is not $B$<br>Some $A$ is not possibly $B$<br>Some $A$ must not be $B$ |
| Possibly all $A$ is $B$<br>All $A$ is possibly $B$<br>All $A$ may be $B$ | Possibly no $A$ is $B$<br>No $A$ is necessarily $B$<br>No $A$ must be $B$ |
| Possibly some $A$ is $B$<br>Some $A$ is possibly $B$<br>Some $A$ may be $B$ | Possibly some $A$ is not $B$<br>Some $A$ is not necessarily $B$<br>Some $A$ may not be $B$ |

In addition to the relations of contradiction holding among propositions 1 to 8 above, relations of implication will be seen to hold also. For example, "Necessarily all $A$ is $B$" implies "Necessarily some $A$ is $B$". We shall refer to this as the *law of subalternation* of the particular apodeictic premiss. Again, "Necessarily all $A$ is $B$" implies "Possibly all $A$ is $B$": we shall call this a *law of modal subordination*. Using Łukasiewicz's symbolism, in which $L$ and $M$ replace "necessarily" and "possibly" when applied *de dicto*, these relations may be summarized in the following "octagon of opposition", in which arrows represent implication and, as before, straight lines join contradictories [1]:

TABLE 6

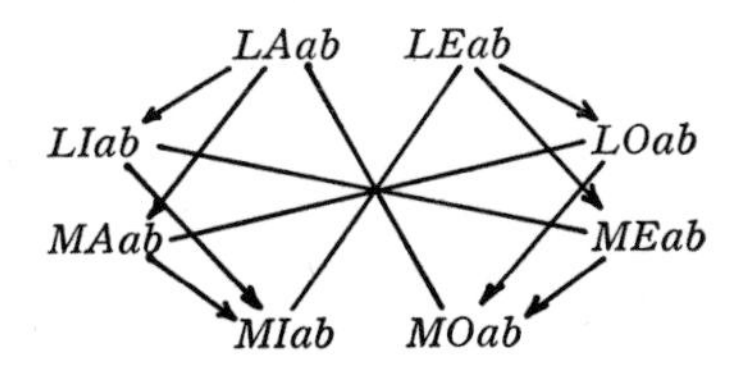


[1] An extended version of this table, with assertoric formulae as well, is to be found in Bochenski, LT, p. 93, where it is described as the "classical" square of opposition for modal propositions.

It is interesting to see just how many of these relations are actually recognized and made use of by Aristotle. Leaving aside the relations of subalternation and subordination for the time being, we find in the chapters on apodeictic syllogisms that Aristotle, in constructing the peculiar variety of "*reductio*" disproof referred to in table 1, makes use of the mutual contradictoriness of *LIba* and *MEba* in 30a25–28, and of *LOac* and *MAac* in 30b29–31. Hence we may safely assume that the contradiction-relations of table 6 are Aristotelian. Nor are the equivalences of table 5 unknown to him. He states the premiss *LEab* sometimes in the form ἀνάγκη το *A* τῷ *B* μηδενὶ ὑπάρχειν (25a29), and sometimes in the form τὸ *A* τῷ *B* οὐδενὶ ἐνδέχεται (30b12), thus showing that he regarded "Necessarily no *A* is *B*" to be the same as "No *A* is possibly *B*". Aristotle was obviously acquainted with the difference in form between modalities *de dicto* and *de re*, though not of course with the phantasmic difference in content.

## 14. Axiomatization of the apodeictic moods. The *L-X-M* calculus

In this section I shall present a set of axioms sufficient for the deduction of all and only those moods with necessary premiss(es) held to be valid by Aristotle. My method will be to assume, as Aristotle does, certain moods as "perfect", i.e. as axioms, and to deduce the others from them. (I intentionally ignore here the problem of whether Aristotle takes certain moods to be "perfect" because they can serve as adequate axioms, or whether he intends them to be "perfect" by some independent criterion.) In addition, certain axioms representing "immediate inferences" (inferences with only one premiss) will be assumed, and also sufficient axioms to derive the system of assertoric syllogisms. This procedure differs from that of Łukasiewicz, who in developing the modal moods assumes no new syllogistic axioms, but only a new system of propositional modal logic, with the aid of which he is able to obtain modal moods from assertoric ones. For the reasons given in sect. 12 I shall assume as "auxiliary theory" only the laws of unmodalized propositional logic. My list of axioms is a long one, but the result of omitting modal propositional laws is a gain in "Aristotelicity" of the system. Łukasiewicz himself finds it "strange" that Aristotle makes practically no use of his theorems of propositional modal logic [1]. The reason is that these theorems simply will not do the job required of them.

The following is the basis of the "$L$–$X$–$M$ calculus".

*Primitive symbols*

Variables: $a, b, c, \ldots$
Functions of one argument: $N, L$
Functions of two arguments: $C, A, I$

*Rules of Formation*

(i) Any formula $A\alpha\beta$ or $I\alpha\beta$, where $\alpha$ and $\beta$ are variables, is well-formed. Such formulae are called *categorical expressions*.

(ii) If $\alpha$ is well-formed, then $N\alpha$ is well-formed. If $\alpha$ is a categorical expression, then $N\alpha$ is a categorical expression.

(iii) If $\alpha$ is a categorical expression, then $L\alpha$ is well-formed.

(iv) If $\alpha$ and $\beta$ are well-formed, then $C\alpha\beta$ is well-formed.

(v) No other formula is well-formed.

*Definitions*

Df $E$: $E = NI$
Df $O$: $O = NA$
Df $M$: $M = NLN$
Df $K$: $K\alpha\beta = NC\alpha N\beta$

*Rules of Inference*

(i) Rule of substitution of variables for variables.

(ii) Rule of *modus ponens:* from $\alpha$ and $C\alpha\beta$, infer $\beta$.

*Axioms*

Four axioms taken over from Łukasiewicz's axiomatization of the assertoric syllogistic, the second of which is strengthened for reasons to appear in sect. 20:

1. $Aaa$
2. $LIaa$
3. $CK\,Abc\,Aab\,Aac$ (Barbara $XXX$)
4. $CK\,Abc\,Iba\;\,Iac$ (Datisi $XXX$);

---

[1] Łukasiewicz, p. 181.

plus four *LXL* moods:

5. *CK LAbc Aab LAac* (Barbara *LXL*)
6. *CK LEcb Aab LEac* (Cesare *LXL*)
7. *CK LAbc Iab LIac* (Darii *LXL*)
8. *CK LEbc Iab LOac* (Ferio *LXL*);

plus two *LLL* moods:

9. *CK LAcb LOab LOac* (Baroco *LLL*)
10. *CK LObc LAba LOac* (Bocardo *LLL*);

plus the law of conversion of the apodeictic *I*-premiss:

11. *C LIab LIba;*

plus three laws of modal subordination:

12. *C LAab Aab*
13. *C LIab Iab*
14. *C LOab Oab.*

*Auxiliary Theory*

As auxiliary theory the two-valued propositional calculus will be used, any well-formed formula of the *L–X–M* calculus being allowed to be substituted for a propositional variable. In the ensuing formal deductions we shall make use of the following propositional theses:

I. *CCKpqrCpCqr*
II. *CCpCqrCqCpr*
III. *CCpqCNqNp*
IV. *CCpqCCqrCpr*
V. *CCKpqrCKNrqNp*
VI. *CCKpqrCKpNrNq*
VII. *CpCqp*

and, for convenience, a rule of double negation (RN), allowing any well-formed formula $\alpha$ to be replaced by $NN\alpha$ and conversely.

## 15. The laws of subalternation

We begin by deducing, firstly, the remaining axiom of Łukasiewicz's basis for assertoric syllogistic (thesis 15), and secondly, the modal laws of subalternation (see table 6), which are logically simpler than some of the laws of conversion.

13=*C*2–15. *Iaa*[1]
I=*C*7–16. *C LAbc C Iab LIac*
II=*C*16–17. *C Iab C LAbc LIac*
17=*C*15–18. *C LAab LIab*
(law of subalternation of *LI*-premiss)
III=*C*18–19. *C NLIab NLAab*
(19, RN, Df *E*, Df *O*, Df *M*) 20. *C MEab MOab*
(law of subalternation of *MO*-premiss)
I=*C*8–21. *C LEbc C Iab LOac*
II=*C*21–*C*15–22. *C LEab LOab*
(law of subalternation of *LO*-premiss)
III=*C*22–23. *C NLOab NLEab*
(23, Df *O*, Df *E*, Df *M*) 24. *C MAab MIab*
(law of subalternation of *MI*-premiss)

There is no explicit statement of these laws in the *Prior Analytics*, yet Aristotle plainly held them to be valid. Thus in attempting to prove the convertibility *per accidens* of the universal apodeictic premiss in 25a32–34, Aristotle says, "If all ... *B* is *A* of necessity, it is necessary also that some *A* is *B*; for if there were no necessity, neither would some of the *B*'s be *A* necessarily". What he is basing his proof on here is the absurdity of supposing "All *B* is necessarily *A*" true, and "Some *B* is necessarily *A*" false. But this is to recognize that the first implies the second.

## 16. The laws of conversion

Having used Darii and Ferio *LXL* to prove the laws of subalternation, we shall now use Cesare *LXL* to prove one of the apodeictic laws of simple conversion. The other must be assumed without proof. Subalternation is then used to prove the laws of conversion *per accidens*.

---

[1] The proof notation is based on that of Łukasiewicz, p. 81. Substitutions are omitted.

11. *C LIab LIba*
(law of conversion of *LI*-premiss)

III=*C*11–25. *C NLIba NLIab*

(25, RN, Df *E*, Df *M*) 26. *C MEab MEba*
(law of conversion of *ME*-premiss)

I=*C*6–27. *C LEcb C Aab LEac*

II=*C*27–*C*1–28. *C LEab LEba*
(law of conversion of *LE*-premiss)

III=*C*28–29. *C NLEba NLEab*

(29, Df *E*, Df *M*) 30. *C MIab MIba*
(law of conversion of *MI*-premiss)

IV=*C*18–*C*11–31. *C LAab LIba*
(law of conversion of *LA*-premiss)

IV=*C*24–*C*30–32. *C MAab MIba*
(law of conversion of *MA*-premiss)

All these laws are recognized and stated by Aristotle. We find the convertibility of the *LE*-premiss in 25a29–31, and of the *LA*- and *LI*-premisses in 25a32–34. In 25a37–25b2 Aristotle says that no matter in which sense the word "possible" is taken, affirmative possible premisses convert as affirmative assertorics do. Thus we have the convertibility of the *MA*- and *MI*-premisses. But in negative statements the case is different; only in the sense of "possible" in which we would be prepared to say that what is necessary is also possible (25b4) is it allowable to proceed from "Possibly no *A* is *B*" to "Possibly no *B* is *A*". But this is the sense of "possible" which we denote by *M;* hence we have the convertibility of the *ME*-premiss. Aristotle gives an example to illustrate this convertibility. If it is possible for no man to be a horse (it being also necessary for no man to be a horse), then it is possible for no horse to be a man. Aristotle completes his survey of the laws of conversion by rejecting the convertibility of the *LO*-premiss (25a34–36) and the *MO*-premiss (25b13–14).

Although his statement of these laws is complete, Aristotle's proof of them is unsatisfactory. He reduces the convertibility of *LEab* to the convertibility of *MIab*, which he says he has already proven (25b2–3), but which he has not. Nor does he seem to offer any proof at all of the convertibility of *LIab*.

## 17. The laws of modal subordination

In this section the various laws of modal subordination will be deduced, completing the system of relations found in table 6. Three of these laws already occur as axioms.

| | | |
|---|---|---|
| 12. | *C LAab Aab* | (law of subordination) |
| 13. | *C LIab Iab* | ( ,, ) |
| 14. | *C LOab Oab* | ( ,, ) |
| III=*C*12–33. | *C NAab NLAab* | |
| (33, RN, Df *O*, Df *M*) 34. | *C Oab MOab* | ( ,, ) |
| III=*C*13–35. | *C NIab NLIab* | |
| (35, RN, Df *E*, Df *M*) 36. | *C Eab MEab* | ( ,, ) |
| III=*C*14–37. | *C NOab NLOab* | |
| (37, Df *O*, RN, Df *M*) 38. | *C Aab MAab* | ( ,, ) |
| 38=*C*1–39. | *MAaa* | |
| II=*C*21–40. | *C Iab C LEbc LOac* | |
| IV=*C*40–*C*III–41. | *C Iab C NLOac NLEbc* | |
| (41, Df *O*, Df *E*, Df *M*) 42. | *C Iab C MAac MIbc* | |
| II=*C*42–*C*39–43. | *C Iab MIba* | |
| IV=*C*43–*C*30–44. | *C Iab MIab* | ( ,, ) |
| III=*C*44–45. | *C NMIab NIab* | |
| (45, Df *M*, Df *E*, RN) 46. | *C LEab Eab* | ( ,, ) |

From these eight laws of modal subordination it is easy to derive the four relations of subordination in table 6. Like the relations of subalternation, these laws are not explicitly mentioned by Aristotle, though there is little doubt that he recognized them. For example, in discussing the mood Celarent with necessary major premiss and contingent minor, Aristotle first shows that these premisses justify the drawing of the assertoric conclusion "*A* belongs to no *C*". He then says that "it is clear that the possibility of not belonging can be inferred, since the fact of not belonging is inferred" (36a15–17). That is, we may infer *MEca* from *Eca*.

## 18. The *LLL*, *LXL* and *XLL* moods

Having now equipped ourselves with the means of deducing one syllogistic mood from another by the use of the laws of conversion, subalternation and subordination, we may proceed to derive

Aristotle's complete system of *LLL*, *LXL* and *XLL* moods from the six "perfect" modal moods assumed as axioms. Actually, we shall do more than this. We saw in sect. 11 that a *reductio ad absurdum* argument allows us to derive from any mood two further moods; thus from Barbara *XXX* we may derive Baroco and Bocardo *XXX*. This method of derivation works for modal moods as well. For example, the following is a proof of Ferison *MXM* and Camestres *LMX* from axiom 7, Darii *LXL:*

7. *CK LAbc Iab LIac* (Darii *LXL*)

V=*C*7–47. *CK NLIac Iab NLAbc*

(47, RN, Df *E*, Df *O*, Df *M*) 149. *CK MEbc Iba MOac* (Ferison *MXM*)

VI=*C*7–48. *CK LAbc NLIac NIab*

(48, RN, Df *E*, Df *M*) 167. *CK LAcb MEab Eac* (Camestres *LMX*)

Although Aristotle makes no mention of moods with possible (as opposed to contingent) premisses, *reductio* proofs similar to the above are fairly common in the *Prior Analytics*. For example, see Aristotle's *reductio* proof of Bocardo *QXM* ("*Q*" denoting contingency), in 39b33–39. It is true that Aristotle never employs a *reductio* argument when the conclusion of the syllogism he wishes to prove valid is a *necessary* proposition. Such a proof would require a *reductio* syllogism with a possible premiss, and the closest that Aristotle comes to acknowledging syllogisms of this sort is in his remark, concerning the invalid Darii *XLL*, that "from the denial of the conclusion nothing impossible results" (30b4): i.e. that there is no valid *XMM*, *MXM*, *LMX* or *MLX* mood whose conclusion contradicts one of the original premisses. This remark suggests that Aristotle knew of syllogisms with possible premisses. Since the very possibility of *reductio* arguments in the apodeictic syllogistic implies their existence, we shall make up for Aristotle's omission of them by including them in our system.

In the following table are listed all the valid moods of certain categories provable from the axioms. A number indicates a thesis [1];

[1] Moods assumed axiomatically are numbered 5–10, and those provable from the axioms begin at 100.

a blank that the mood in question is not provable. Proofs are by conversion, subalternation and *reductio ad absurdum*. An *LLL* mood is provable from each valid *LXL* or *XLL* mood by modal subordination except in the case of Baroco and Bocardo *LLL*, which must be assumed as axioms.

TABLE 7

| | | *LLL* | *LXL* | *XLL* | *MXM* | *XMM* | *LMX* | *MLX* |
|---|---|---|---|---|---|---|---|---|
| First figure | Barbara | 100 | 5 | | | | | |
| | Celarent | 101 | 122 | | | | 164 | 179 |
| | Darii | 102 | 7 | | 141 | 157 | | |
| | Ferio | 103 | 8 | | 142 | | 165 | |
| Second figure | Cesare | 104 | 6 | | | | 166 | 180 |
| | Camestres | 105 | | 133 | | | 167 | 181 |
| | Festino | 106 | 123 | | 143 | | 168 | |
| | Baroco | 9 | | | | | 169 | |
| Third figure | Darapti | 107 | 124 | 134 | 144 | 158 | | |
| | Felapton | 108 | 125 | | 145 | | 170 | |
| | Disamis | 109 | | 135 | 146 | 159 | | |
| | Datisi | 110 | 126 | | 147 | 160 | | |
| | Bocardo | 10 | | | 148 | | | |
| | Ferison | 111 | 127 | | 149 | | 171 | |
| Fourth figure | Bramantip | 112 | | 136 | 150 | 161 | | |
| | Camenes | 113 | | 137 | | | 172 | 182 |
| | Dimaris | 114 | | 138 | 151 | 162 | | |
| | Fresison | 115 | 128 | | 152 | | 173 | |
| | Fesapo | 116 | 129 | | 153 | | 174 | |
| Subaltern moods | Barbari | 117 | 130 | | 154 | 163 | | |
| | Celaront | 118 | 131 | | 155 | | 175 | 183 |
| | Cesaro | 119 | 132 | | 156 | | 176 | 184 |
| | Camestrop | 120 | | 139 | | | 177 | 185 |
| | Camenop | 121 | | 140 | | | 178 | 186 |

For the sake of completeness, fourth figure and subaltern moods are included in this table, although they are not of course dealt with by Aristotle. The only moods which *are* considered by him are enclosed within dotted lines in the top left hand corner of the table, and it is only here that there is an opportunity of measuring the degree of exactitude with which the $L$–$X$–$M$ system "fits" Aristotle's. As may be seen by comparing table 7 with table 1, this degree of exactitude – the system's "Aristotelicity" – is perfect.

## 19. Further *L-X-M* moods

We have not yet exhausted the forms which may be assumed by $L$-$X$-$M$ syllogisms. Since we may have for each of the two premisses and the conclusion a necessary, an assertoric or a possible proposition, there exist in all 27 different forms of $L$-$X$-$M$ syllogism, namely;

*LLL, LLX, LXL, XLL, LXX, XLX, XXL, XXX,*
*LLM, LML, MLL, LMM, MLM, MML, MMM,*
*XXM, XMX, MXX, XMM, MXM, MMX,*
*LXM, XLM, LMX, MLX, XML, MXL.*

Of these, 9 pairs (appearing side by side in the above list) differ only in the order in which their premisses are written: disregarding this difference for the moment, we are left with 18 types. Among these 18, some may be proved to be equivalent to others by *reductio* arguments. Thus to every *LLL* mood there correspond two equivalent *reductio* moods of the forms *LMM* and *MLM;* of the 18 types, we may therefore regard the two types *LLL* and *LMM*/*MLM* as equivalent. Letting $L$ take precedence, I shall choose *LMM* as the representative of the second of these types, and write $LLL \leftrightarrow LMM$. Equivalences of this sort reduce the number of distinct syllogistic types to 10.

Not only equivalences, but also relations of implication hold between syllogistic types. For example, by weakening the conclusion of Barbara *LXL* we obtain Barbara *LXX*, or by strengthening the minor premiss we get Barbara *LLL*. I shall write $LXL \rightarrow LXX$, $LXL \rightarrow LLL$, etc., and incorporate these relations of equivalence and implication into the following table:

TABLE 8

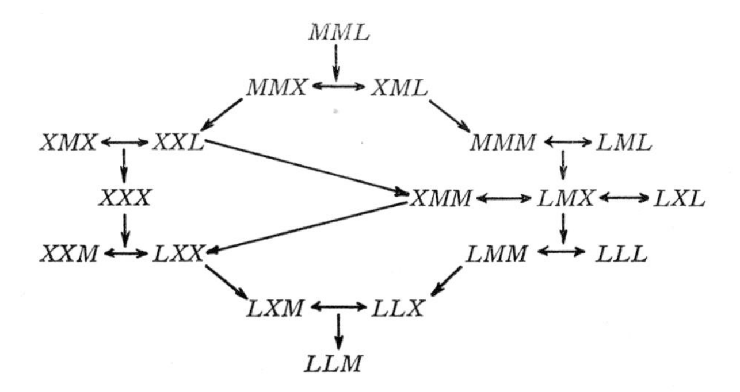


Table 8 gives a picture of the intricate and elegant structure of modal syllogisms. It remains to see which moods of each syllogistic type are valid.

There are 24 valid *XXX* moods and from these may be derived by modal subordination 24 *LXX*, 24 *XLX*, and 24 *XXM* moods; from these 24 *LLX* [1], 24 *LXM* and 24 *XLM* moods, and from these in turn 24 *LLM* moods. Next, we see from table 7 that there are 23 valid moods of each of the types *LXL*/*XLL*, *MXM*/*XMM* and *LMX*/*MLX*; these moods are "fragmentary" in the sense of sect. 12. However, the *LLL* moods are not fragmentary, and it may be shown that this lack of fragmentation carries over into the *LMM* and *MLM* moods. For take any *LMM* mood with a valid *XXX* counterpart, e.g. Cesare *LMM*. A look at table 4 will show that Cesare *LMM* is a *reductio* mood of Ferio *LLL*, and hence provable from it. The same will hold for any one of the *LMM* or *MLM* counterparts of the 24 valid *XXX* moods; there will always be a means of exchanging either the major or the minor premiss with the conclusion and thereby reducing it to one of the valid *LLL* moods. Hence the number of valid *LMM* and *MLM* moods will each be 24.

This completes the total of valid *L–X–M* moods. We shall not add any *MMM* moods, as Łukasiewicz does [2]: these moods occur

---

[1] For a hint that Aristotle might repudiate *LLX* moods, see chapter 12 of *An. pr.* I.

[2] Łukasiewicz, p. 193.

above the *LXL* moods in table 8, and so are not implied by any of our axioms. Even if they might have been acceptable to Aristotle, it is unlikely that their *LML* and *MLL* counterparts would have been, as Łukasiewicz himself recognises. Hence we are left with the following valid moods:

| | |
|---|---|
| *LXL/XLL, XMM/MXM, LMX/MLX* . | 3 × 23 = 69 |
| *XXX, LXX, XLX, XXM, LLL, LMM,* | |
| *MLM, LLX, LXM, XLM, LLM* . . . . | 11 × 24 = 264 |
| Total valid *L–X–M* moods . . . . . . . . . . | 333. |

## CHAPTER III

# DECISION PROCEDURE FOR THE APODEICTIC MOODS

## 20. The mechanism of rejection

In this chapter there will be established a *decision procedure* by which we may determine, given any formula of the $L$–$X$–$M$ calculus, (a) whether or not it is a theorem, and (b) if it is a theorem, how to prove it. The key notion upon which this procedure is based is the notion of *rejection*.

It was Łukasiewicz who, among modern logicians, first gave formal recognition to the concept of rejection [1]. But, as Łukasiewicz points out, Aristotle was equally aware of its importance, and went to considerable lengths not only to prove the valid moods of his syllogistic, but also to disprove the invalid ones. This is shown by the fact that, among the 15 invalid apodeictic moods of table 1, only one, namely Festino $XLL$, is not explicitly rejected, i.e. shown to be invalid, by Aristotle. There seems little doubt that he attached great importance to the rejection of invalid moods, and we should do likewise.

The decision procedure for the $L$–$X$–$M$ calculus will take the following form. Conforming to Łukasiewicz's pattern in treating assertoric syllogisms, there will be laid down a set of axiomatic rejections, and rules of rejection, of such a kind that every formula of the calculus that is not provable may be demonstrably rejected. When this is done, we may say that our axiomatic basis for the $L$–$X$–$M$ calculus is *complete*.

The desirability of a procedure by which we may either prove or demonstrably reject syllogistic expressions becomes acute when we consider modal sorites. For example, consider the rather simple

---

[1] See Łukasiewicz, p. 94 ff.

sorites:

$$CKKK\ MAab\ LEbd\ Aed\ Ice\ MOac$$

This sorites is not in fact provable from the axioms and rules of the *L–X–M* calculus, but that this is so is not immediately obvious. For more complicated sorites our difficulties increase. What is needed is firstly a means of rejecting false expressions, and secondly a means of separating rejected from asserted or true expressions.

For rejecting false expressions of the *L–X–M* calculus the following three rules of rejection, used by Łukasiewicz for assertoric syllogisms, are required:

(i) Rule of rejection by detachment: if the implication $C\alpha\beta$ is asserted, but the consequent $\beta$ is rejected, then the antecedent $\alpha$ must be rejected too. In symbols, indicating rejected expressions by an asterisk:

$$C\alpha\beta,\ {}^*\beta \rightarrow {}^*\alpha.$$

(ii) Rule of rejection by substitution: if $\beta$ is a substitution of $\alpha$, and $\beta$ is rejected, then $\alpha$ must be rejected too.

(iii) Słupecki's rule of rejection: if $\alpha$ and $\beta$ are simple negative expressions and $\gamma$ is an elementary expression, then if $C\alpha\gamma$ and $C\beta\gamma$ are rejected, $C\alpha C\beta\gamma$ must be rejected too. In symbols:

$${}^*C\alpha\gamma,\ {}^*C\beta\gamma \rightarrow {}^*C\alpha C\beta\gamma.$$

Before explaining the terminology used in the statement of Słupecki's rule, it may be noted that Aristotle seems to make occasional use of the rule of rejection by detachment. For example in 31b20–27 he disproves Datisi *XLL* by converting it to Darii *XLL*, which he has already rejected. However he shows his ignorance of the proper use of this rule by attempting a similar disproof of Felapton *XLL*, which he converts per accidens to the rejected Ferio *XLL*. What he ignores is that, unlike the case of Darii and Datisi, Ferio implies Felapton but not vice versa, so that it might very well be that Ferio is false or invalid, and Felapton true or valid. That is, the invalidity of Ferio cannot be used to demonstrate the invalidity of Felapton.

Now for the terminology used in Słupecki's rule. All expressions of the *L–X–M* calculus which do not contain the operators *C* or *K* are reducible, by the definitions of *E*, *O* and *M* and by double negation, to one of the twelve forms *LAab*, *LIab*, *Aab*, *Iab*, *MAab*, *MIab*, *LEab*, *LOab*, *Eab*, *Oab*, *MEab* and *MOab*, which are called *simple expressions* [1]. Of these the first six are *simple affirmative expressions*, and the last six *simple negative expressions*. Together with simple expressions, expressions of the type:

$$C\alpha_1\, C\alpha_2\, C\alpha_3 \ldots C\alpha_{n-1}\alpha_n,$$

where the $\alpha$'s are simple expressions, are called *elementary expressions*. A good explanation of the rationale of Słupecki's rule is given by Łukasiewicz on p. 104, in which he points out that in certain cases we can obtain from the conjunction of two positive premisses, or of a positive and a negative premiss, a conclusion which does not result from either of them separately (e.g. *Eac* follows from *Ebc* and *Aab*, although both *C Ebc Eac* and *C Aab Eac* are rejected). On the other hand, nothing can be inferred from two negative premisses that does not follow from one of them alone (e.g. *Obc* follows from *Ebc*, and *Eba* from *Eab*, but nothing new follows from their conjunction). Hence if each negative expression fails to imply a conclusion separately, their conjunction as implying that conclusion must be rejected.

Rejection also requires axiomatic rejections, from which we start. I shall not at this point give all the axiomatic rejections which we need for the *L–X–M* calculus, but simply the following two:

*1. *C LAaa MOaa*

*2. *C LEab LAaa*

Starting from this basis we shall now proceed to reject all simple expressions which are not theorems of the *L–X–M* calculus. To begin with we must consider which simple expressions are theorems. We note that the simple expression *LIaa* was assumed as an axiom, from which the theorem *Iaa* was derived immediately by use of the axiom *C LIab Iab*. The reason why we assumed *LIaa* and not *Iaa* will become clear later on; as we shall see, our calculations will be

[1] Note that we may have $a = b$, so that *LAaa* is also a simple expression.

somewhat simplified by reason of it. The expression *LAaa*, however, is *not* a theorem. If it were, the direst consequences would follow, among them the possibility of detaching the consequent *C Aab LAab* of the following substituted form of Barbara *LXL:*

*C LAbb C Aab LAab*,

and hence being able to prove the equivalence of *Aab* and *LAab* – the collapse of all modal distinctions whatsoever. On the other hand, we may now see why it would not do to say that *LAaa* was *false* for all values of *a*. In that case *NLAaa*, i.e. *MOaa*, would be a theorem, and as a result we could detach the consequent *C Aab MOab* of the following substituted form of Bocardo *MXM:;*

*C MObb C Aab MOab*.

Transposing *C Aab MOab* yields *C LAab Oab*, a quite un-Aristotelian thesis. Hence both *LAaa* and *MOaa* must be rejected. The situation, however, is not the same in the case of *LIaa*. No awkward consequences follow from assuming *LIaa* to be true, and so for convenience we assume it. From it and *Aaa* and the laws of modal subordination we may easily prove all the other simple affirmative expressions whose two variables are identified except *LAaa*. The rejection of the remaining simple expressions proceeds as follows:

VII=*C**3–*2

*3. *LAaa*

VII=*C**4–*1

*4. *MOaa*

20=*C**5–*4

*5. *MEaa*

Similarly, using the various rules of subalternation and modal subordination, we may reject *Oaa*, *Eaa*, *LOaa*, *LEaa*. Continuing we get:

(*4, *a*/*b*) *6. *MOab*,

from which *MEab*, *Oab*, *Eab*, *LOab*, *LEab* may be rejected. We also have:

(III) 187. *CC MOaa MIab C NMIab NMOaa*
(187, Df *M*, Df *E*, Df *O*, RN) 188. *CC MOaa MIab C LEab LAaa*

188=*C**7–*2

*7. *C MOaa MIab*

VII=*C**8–*7

*8. *MIab*,

from which *MAab, Iab, Aab, LIab, LAab* may be rejected. This completes our rejection of all simple expressions of the *L–X–M* calculus which are not theorems.

## 21. A decision procedure for the *L-X-M* calculus

Having seen how the process of rejection proceeds, we may now pass to the establishment of a decision procedure for the *L–X–M* calculus, in the course of which the remainder of the required axiomatic rejections will be given. Our decision procedure is based upon a definition and a theorem due to Łukasiewicz, which I shall now state. The definition is of what Łukasiewicz calls *deductive equivalence*, and is to be found in Łukasiewicz p. 110:

"Two expressions are deductively equivalent to each other with respect to certain theses when and only when we can prove by means of these theses and of the rules of inference that if one of those expressions is asserted, the other must be asserted too, or if one of them is rejected, the other must be rejected too".

We now state the theorem upon which the possibility of a decision procedure for the *L–X–M* calculus depends. Adapting Łukasiewicz's statement of it on p. 111 for our purposes, it reads as follows:

"Every significant expression of the *L–X–M* calculus can be reduced in a deductively equivalent way, with respect to theses of the propositional calculus, to one or more elementary expressions, i.e. expressions of the form

$$C\alpha_1\, C\alpha_2\, \ldots\, C\alpha_{n-1}\alpha_n,$$

where all the $\alpha$'s are simple expressions, i.e. expressions of the type *LAab, LEab, LIab, LOab, Aab, Eab, Iab, Oab, MAab, MEab, MIab*, or *MOab*".

What this theorem gives us, in effect, is a standard form of expression in the *L–X–M* calculus whose instances we may examine with the view of determining whether they are provable or rejected. Any instance of this standard form is always an elementary expression. Every expression in the *L–X–M* calculus is reducible to it in the sense of being reducible to one or more elementary expressions, each of which may be examined separately. If it or they are all asserted, then the original expression is asserted, and if it or one of them is rejected, then the original expression is rejected. I shall not prove Łukasiewicz's theorem. Its proof proceeds as on pp. 111–120 of *Aristotle's Syllogistic*, the only difference being that for modal syllogistic the number of elementary expressions is larger than for assertoric syllogistic. Once the theorem is proved, however, we may in our establishment of a decision procedure base our arguments upon the consideration of elementary expressions alone, knowing that all other expressions of the *L–X–M* calculus can be reduced to them.

We may now specify the procedure for determining whether any expression of the form:

$$(1)\ C\alpha_1 C\alpha_2 \ldots C\alpha_{n-1}\alpha_n$$

is a theorem or rejected. Our first task is to consider simple expressions, and this has already been done in showing that every simple expression is either a theorem or rejected on the basis of the two axiomatic rejections *1 and *2. Compound elementary expressions, with one or more antecedents, must now be investigated. Several different cases present themselves, and will be examined in turn. Proofs will be largely informal.

*Case* 1. The consequent $\alpha_n$ is negative, and all antecedents are affirmative. Such expressions are rejected.

*Proof*. Identify all variables with *a*, and thus obtain a new expression (2) in place of the original expression (1). We have as possible antecedents in (2) the expressions *LAaa*, *LIaa*, *Aaa*, *Iaa*, *MAaa* and *MIaa*, and as possible consequents the expressions *LEaa*, *LOaa*, *Eaa*, *Oaa*, *MEaa*, *MOaa*. Replacing each antecedent by the strongest, *LAaa*, and the conclusion by the weakest, *MOaa*, we get instead of (2) a new expression

$$(3)\quad C\, LAaa\, C\, LAaa\, \ldots\, C\, LAaa\, MOaa,$$

which is entailed by (2) through repeated applications of the laws *CCpqCCqrCpr*, *CCqrCCpqCpr*, and the law of commutation of antecedents *CCpCqrCqCpr*. Finally, by repeated application of the law *CCpCpqCpq* we see that (3) implies

$$*1.\quad C\, LAaa\, MOaa,$$

which is rejected. Hence (2), which implies it, will also be rejected, and with it the original expression (1), of which (2) is a substitution.

*Case* 2. The consequent is negative, and only one antecedent is negative. This case may be reduced to the case where antecedents and consequent are alike affirmative (Case 5), which is shown to be decidable below.

*Proof*. Replace each simple negative expression $\alpha_i$ by an expression of the form $N\beta_i$, where $\beta_i$ is a simple affirmative expression, by using the definitions of *E*, *O*, and *M*, and double negation. By commuting antecedents we can then write (1) in the form

$$(2)\quad C\alpha_j\, C\alpha_k\, \ldots\, CN\beta_i N\beta_n,$$

where $\beta_i$ and $\beta_n$ are simple affirmative expressions. Now expressions of the form $C\alpha CN\beta N\gamma$ are deductively equivalent to expressions of the form $C\alpha C\gamma\beta$ with respect to the theses *CCpCNrNqCpCqr* and *CCpCqrCpCNrNq*, this being true for any number of antecedents $\alpha$. Hence (2) is deductively equivalent to

$$(3)\quad C\alpha_j\, C\alpha_k\, \ldots\, C\beta_n\beta_i,$$

in which every element is affirmative.

*Case* 3. The consequent is negative, and more than one antecedent is negative. Such expressions are reduced to simpler expressions, each falling under Case 2, on the basis of which the original expression is decidable. This case requires the use of Słupecki's rule of rejection.

*Proof*. Replace each negative antecedent $\alpha_i$ by $N\beta_i$, where $\beta_i$ is affirmative. By commuting antecedents, we can write (1) in the form

$$(2)\quad CN\beta_i\, CN\beta_j\, C\alpha_k \ldots \alpha_n.$$

From this expression we form two simpler expressions:

$$(3)\quad CN\beta_i\, C\alpha_k \ldots \alpha_n$$

$$\text{and}\quad (4)\quad CN\beta_j\, C\alpha_k \ldots \alpha_n.$$

If these expressions have more negative antecedents than one we repeat the same procedure until we get formulae with only one negative antecedent. All such formulae fall under Case 2, and are accordingly either asserted or rejected. If only one of them is asserted, the original expression (1) must be asserted too, for by repeated applications of the law of simplification $CpCqp$ we can add to this asserted formula all the other negative antecedents which were previously omitted. If, however, all the formulae with one negative antecedent are rejected, repeated application of Słupecki's rule of rejection will show that (1) must be rejected too.

*Case* 4. The consequent is affirmative, and some (or all) antecedents are negative. This case reduces to Case 3.

*Proof.* By commuting antecedents so that the last is a negative expression $\alpha_i$, and by replacing $\alpha_i$ by $N\beta_i$, we may write (1) in the form

$$(2)\quad C\alpha_j\, C\alpha_k \ldots CN\beta_i\alpha_n.$$

Now expressions of the form $C\alpha CN\beta\gamma$ are deductively equivalent to expressions of the form $C\alpha CN\beta CN\gamma Oaa$ with respect to the theses $CCpCNqrCpCNqCNrOaa$ and $CCpCNqCNrOaaCpCNqr$, $Oaa$ being a proposition that is always false, i.e. whose contradictory is a theorem. Since this is true for any number of antecedents $\alpha$, (2) is deductively equivalent to

$$(3)\quad C\alpha_j\, C\alpha_k \ldots CN\beta_i\, CN\alpha_n\, Oaa,$$

which is decidable using Case 3.

All the cases with negative elements are now exhausted, and in what follows it is assumed that no negative elements are present. The case with affirmative elements will be subdivided according to the character of the consequent. In what follows we shall assume that only the variables $a$, $b_1$, $b_2$ ... $b_n$ and $c$ occur in the original expression (1).

*Case* 5.11. The consequent is *LIaa, Aaa, Iaa, MAaa* or *MIaa*. The expression is asserted, its consequent being always true.

*Case* 5.12. The consequent is *LAaa*. If (a) we have among the antecedents *LAaa*, or an expression *LAca* and a chain leading from $a$ to $c$ valid with respect to the conclusion *Aac* (an *Aac*-chain), the expression is asserted. Otherwise (b) it is rejected.

*Proof*. (a) By a chain leading from $a$ to $c$ we shall understand a sequence of universal affirmative premisses, each one of which may be either necessary, assertoric or problematic, of the following kind:

$$ZAab_1, ZAb_1b_2, \ldots ZAb_{n-1}b_n, ZAb_nc;$$

where $Z$ is an operator taking the values $L$, $X$ or $M$ indifferently. I shall say that such a chain is valid with respect to the conclusion *ZAac* (or is, in short, a *ZAac*-chain) if and only if the expression *ZAac* results from the chain either immediately, or by repeated application of some mood or moods Barbara *ZZZ*. For example, the chain

$$LAab_1, MAb_1b_2, LAb_2c;$$

and the degenerate chain *Aac* are both *MAac*-chains, the former through application of the moods Barbara *MLM* and *LMM*. It is evident that an *LAac*-chain will also be an *Aac*- and an *MAac*-chain.

In our present case we require an *Aac*-chain, and this will be seen to be one containing only *L*'s and *X*'s, since examination of the various valid Barbara moods shows that any containing *M*-premisses have at best only an *M*-conclusion. Given an *Aac*-chain, we may demonstrate that combining its consequent with the expression *LAca* gives the desired result by means of the following substitution $b/c$, $c/a$ in Barbara *LXL:*

$$CK\ LAca\ Aac\ LAaa.$$

(b) To prove that, lacking the above requirements, the expression must be rejected, identify the variables $b_i$ (or $c$) in all antecedents of the form $LAb_ia$ (or *LAca*) with the new variable $b$. This substitution of variables will not result in there being created any antecedent of the form $Aab$, nor any antecedent implying $Aab$, since, if we had had both $Aab_i$ and $LAb_ia$ among the original antecedents, the original expression (1) would have been asserted in virtue of the above substituted form of Barbara $LXL$. Similarly if we had had any expression stronger than $Aab_i$. I shall abbreviate these instructions and remarks in future by stating that when we put $b_i = b$ for all $LAb_ia$, we get no $Aab$, since $Aab_i \, LAb_ia \Rightarrow LAaa$. (The last expression is simply an abbreviation of '$CK \, Aab_i \, LAb_ia \, LAaa$'.)

Continuing, identify the rest of the variables (other than $a$ and $b$) now remaining in the original expression with the variable $c$. We get no $LAca$, since there are no expressions of the forms $LAb_ia$ or $LAca$ left, nor $Acb$, since $Ab_ib_j \, LAb_ja \Rightarrow LAb_ia$. This last step requires some explanation. I shall assume in dealing with rejection that, before I begin substituting for variables in the original expression, all the implications that *can* be drawn among the antecedents are actually drawn, and the consequences of such implications added to the antecedents. Thus I shall assume in the above case that if we had had the antecedent $Ab_ib_j$, and the antecedent $LAb_ja$, we should also have had the antecedent $LAb_ia$ which the first two imply. Hence when we put $b_j = b$ (because of $LAb_ja$), we shall also automatically put $b_i = b$ (because of the implied $LAb_ia$), thus leaving no expression $Acb$ when we substitute the variable $c$. Note that the rejection of the lengthened original expression (containing the consequents of all implications drawn among its antecedents) entails the rejection of the original expression itself in virtue of the law $CCpqCCprCKpqr$.

After performing these two substitutions we may write down the substituted form of our original expression. It would, however, be tedious to consider every possible form this expression could take, and accordingly I shall write down only the *strongest* possible combination of antecedents with which our substitutions leave us. Bearing in mind that we may not have $LAaa$, $Aab$, $LAca$ or $Acb$, since if we did our original expression would have been asserted, this combination, together with the consequent of the original assertion, is as follows:

(2) *Aaa LIaa LAbb LAcc MAab LAba LAac Aca LAbc MAcb* ⇒ *LAaa*

What we wish is to reject (2), and hence reject our original expression (1), of a lengthened and strengthened version of which (2) is a substitution. Certain simplifications in (2) are possible. The antecedents *Aaa* and *LIaa* may be omitted as true, since, in virtue of the law of *modus ponens CpCCpqq*, if *p* is true, in order to reject *Cpq* it suffices to reject *q*. Again, if two of the antecedents of (2) together imply a third, the third may be omitted in virtue of the law *C CKpqr C CKKpqrs CKpqs*, which says in effect that if *Kpq* implies *r*, then in order to reject *CKKpqrs* it suffices to reject *CKpqs*. Among the antecedents of (2) we find the following mutual implications:

*LAba LAac* ⇒ *LAbc* (Barbara *LLL*)
*LAac Aca* ⇒ *LAcc* (subs. of Barbara *LXL*)
*LAac MAcb* ⇒ *MAab* (Barbara *MLM*).

Hence in order to reject our original expression it suffices to reject:

*5.12 *LAbb LAba LAac Aca MAcb* ⇒ *LAaa*.

This expression must be included among our axiomatic rejections.

*Case* 5.21. The consequent is *LAac*, and the antecedents do not include *LAcc*. If (a) there is $LAb_ic$ and an $Aab_i$-chain, the expression is asserted. Otherwise (b) it is rejected.

*Proof*. (a) The combination of $LAb_ic$ and $Aab_i$ yields *LAac* by Barbara *LXL*. What constitutes an $Aab_i$-chain was explained in Case 5.12.

(b) Put $b_i = b$ for all $LAb_ic$. We get no *Aab*, since $Aab_i\ LAb_ic \Rightarrow$ ⇒ *LAac*, nor *Acb*, since $Acb_i\ LAb_ic \Rightarrow LAcc$. Identify the remainder of the variables with *a*. We get no *LAac*, since no $LAb_ic$ are left, nor *Aab*, since $Ab_ib_j\ LAb_jc \Rightarrow LAb_ic$. As usual taking the strongest combination of antecedents, and omitting, as we shall do from now on, all true antecedents such as *Acc* and *LIcc*, we are left with:

(2) *LAaa LAbb MAab LAba Aac LAca LAbc MAcb* ⇒ *LAac*,

which in virtue of the implications:

*MAab LAca* ⇒ *MAcb*, *Aac LAca* ⇒ *LAaa*,
*LAca LAbc* ⇒ *LAba*,

reduces to:

$$*5.21 \quad LAbb\, MAab\, Aac\, LAca\, LAbc \Rightarrow LAac.$$

*Case* 5.22. The consequent is $LAac$, and $LAcc$ is present. If (a) there is an $Aac$-chain, the expression is asserted. Otherwise (b) it is rejected.

*Proof*. (a) $Aac$ and $LAcc$ when combined yield $LAac$ by a substitution of Barbara $LXL$. Cases 5.21 and 5.22 constitute the description of an $LAac$-chain.

(b) Put $b_i = c$ for all $Ab_ic$ (and hence for all $LAb_ic$ too, since if the latter is present what it implies will be present also). There results no $Aac$, since $Aab_i\, Ab_ic \Rightarrow Aac$. Identify all other variables with $a$. Again no $Aac$, since no $Ab_ic$ remain. We are left with:

$$*5.22 \quad LAaa\, LAcc\, MAac\, LAca \Rightarrow LAac.$$

*Case* 5.3. The consequent is $Aac$. If (a) there is an $Aac$-chain, the expression is asserted. Otherwise (b) it is rejected.

*Proof*. (b) Put $b_i = c$ for all $Ab_ic$. We get no $Aac$, since $Aab_i\, Ab_ic \Rightarrow Aac$. Identify all other variables with $a$. We get no $Aac$, since no $Ab_ic$ are left. There remains:

$$*5.3 \quad LAaa\, LAcc\, MAac\, LAca \Rightarrow Aac.$$

Because of the law $CCqrCCpqCpr$, the rejection of *5.3 entails the rejection of *5.22. Hence *5.22 is superfluous.

*Case* 5.41. The consequent is $MAac$, and $LAcc$ is not present. If (a) there is an $Aac$-chain, or $MAb_ic$ and an $LAab_i$-chain, or $MAab_j$ and an $LAb_jc$-chain, or $MAb_ib_j$ and an $LAab_i$- and an $LAb_jc$-chain, the expression is asserted. Otherwise (b) it is rejected.

*Proof*. (a) $MAb_ic$ and $LAab_i$ give $MAac$ by Barbara $MLM$, $MAab_j$ and $LAb_jc$ give it by Barbara $LMM$, and $MAb_ib_j$, $LAab_i$ and $LAb_jc$ give it by both moods together.

(b) Put $b_i = a$ for all $LAab_i$. We get no $MAac$ (since $MAb_ic$ $LAab_i \Rightarrow MAac$). Put $b_i = d$ for all $Aab_i$. No $LAad$ (since no $LAab_i$ left), nor $Adc$ (since $Ab_ic\, Aab_i \Rightarrow Aac$), nor $LAdd$ (since $LAb_ib_i\, Aab_i \Rightarrow LAab_i$). Put $b_i = f$ for all $LAb_ic$. We get no $MAaf$ (since $MAab_i\, LAb_ic \Rightarrow MAac$), nor $Acf$ (since $Acb_i\, LAb_ic \Rightarrow LAcc$), nor $Adf$ (since $Ab_jb_i\, Aab_j \Rightarrow Aab_i$). Put $b_i = e$ for all $Ab_ic$. We get no $Aae$ (none left), nor $LAec$ (none left), nor $Ade$ (since $Ab_jb_i\, Aab_j \Rightarrow$ $\Rightarrow Aab_i$), nor $Aef$ (since $Ab_ib_j\, LAb_jc \Rightarrow LAb_ic$). Finally, identify all other variables with $b$. We get no $Aab$ nor $Abc$ (none left), nor $Adb$ (since $Ab_jb_i\, Aab_j \Rightarrow Aab_i$), nor $Abe$ (since $Ab_ib_j\, Ab_jc \Rightarrow Ab_ic$), nor $Abf$ (since $Ab_ib_j\, LAb_jc \Rightarrow LAb_ic$). We are left with the following expression:

(2) $LAaa\ LAbb\ LAee\ LAff\ MAab\ LAba\ LAca\ Aad\ LAda\ MAae$ $LAea\ LAfa\ MAbc\ LAcb\ LAbd\ MAdb\ MAbe\ LAeb\ MAbf\ LAfb\ LAcd$ $MAdc\ LAce\ Aec\ MAcf\ LAfc\ MAde\ LAed\ MAdf\ LAfd\ MAef\ LAfe$ $\Rightarrow MAac$,

which in virtue of the following implications:

$Aad\ LAda \Rightarrow LAaa$, $LAda\ MAae \Rightarrow MAde$,
$LAda\ LAbd \Rightarrow LAba$, $LAcb\ LAbd \Rightarrow LAcd$,
$LAcb\ Aec \Rightarrow LAeb$, $LAcb\ LAfc \Rightarrow LAfb$,
$LAbd\ MAdf \Rightarrow MAbf$, $LAce\ Aec \Rightarrow LAee$,
$LAce\ LAfc \Rightarrow LAfe$, $LAfc\ MAdf \Rightarrow MAdc$;

$LAba\ MAae \Rightarrow MAbe$, $LAba\ LAcb \Rightarrow LAca$,
$LAba\ LAeb \Rightarrow LAea$, $LAba\ LAfb \Rightarrow LAfa$,
$MAae\ LAeb \Rightarrow MAab$, $LAcb\ MAbf \Rightarrow MAcf$,
$LAbd\ LAeb \Rightarrow LAed$, $LAbd\ LAfb \Rightarrow LAfd$,
$LAeb\ MAde \Rightarrow MAdb$, $MAbf\ LAfc \Rightarrow MAbc$;

$LAed\ MAdf \Rightarrow MAef$;

is reducible to:

*5.41 $LAbb\ LAff\ Aad\ LAda\ MAae\ LAcb\ LAbd\ LAce\ Aec$ $LAfc\ MAdf \Rightarrow MAac$.

*Case* 5.42. The consequent is $MAac$, and $LAcc$ is present. If (a) there is one of the favourable conditions of Case 5.41, or $MAab_j$ and an $Ab_jc$-chain, or $MAb_ib_j$ and an $LAab_i$- and an $Ab_jc$-chain, then the expression is asserted. Otherwise (b) it is rejected.

*Proof*. (a) An $Ab_jc$-chain and $LAcc$ together yield an $LAb_jc$-chain, and the arguments of Case 5.41 apply. Cases 5.41 and 5.42 together constitute the description of an $MAac$-chain.

(b) Put $b_i = a$ for all $LAab_i$. We get no $MAac$ (since $MAb_ic$ $LAab_i \Rightarrow MAac$). Put $b_i = c$ for all $LAb_ic$. No $MAac$ (since $MAab_i\ LAb_ic \Rightarrow MAac$). Put $b_i = d$ for all $Aab_i$. No $LAad$ (none left), nor $Adc$ (since $Ab_ic\ Aab_i \Rightarrow Aac$), nor $LAdd$ (since $LAb_ib_i$ $Aab_i \Rightarrow LAab_i$). Identify all other variables with $b$. No $Aab$ (none left), nor $Abc$ (since $Ab_ic\ LAcc \Rightarrow LAb_ic$), nor $Adb$ (since $Ab_jb_i$ $Aab_j \Rightarrow Aab_i$). We are left with:

(2) $LAaa\ LAbb\ LAcc\ MAab\ LAba\ LAca\ Aad\ LAda\ MAbc\ LAcb$ $LAbd\ MAdb\ LAcd\ MAdc \Rightarrow MAac$,

among whose antecedents the following implications hold:

$$MAab\ LAda \Rightarrow MAdb, \qquad Aad\ \ LAda \Rightarrow LAaa,$$
$$LAda\ LAbd \Rightarrow LAba, \qquad LAcb\ LAbd \Rightarrow LAcd,$$
$$LAbd\ MAdc \Rightarrow MAbc;$$

$$LAda\ LAcd \Rightarrow LAca.$$

In virtue of these implications (2) may be reduced to:

*5.42 $LAbb\ LAcc\ MAab\ Aad\ LAda\ LAcb\ LAbd\ MAdc \Rightarrow MAac$.

*Case* 5.511. The consequent is $LIac$, and the antecedents include neither $LAaa$ nor $LAcc$, though they do include both $Aac$ and $Aca$. If (a) any antecedent $LAb_ia$ or $LAb_ic$ (or both) is present, the expression is asserted. Otherwise (b) it is rejected.

*Proof*. (a) Suppose we have $LAb_ia$ among the antecedents. Then, since $LAb_ia\ Aac \Rightarrow Ab_ic$ (Barbara $XLX$), we have $Ab_ic\ LAb_ia \Rightarrow$ $LIac$ (Darapti $XLL$), so that the expression is asserted. A similar argument applies if the antecedents include $LAb_ic$.

(b) Identify all variables other than $a$ and $c$ with $b$. We get no $LAba$ nor $LAbc$, since no antecedents $LAb_ia$ or $LAb_ic$ are present. This leaves:

(2) $LAbb\ LAab\ Aba\ Aac\ Aca\ Abc\ LAcb \Rightarrow LIac$,

which, in virtue of the implications:

$$LAab\ Aca \Rightarrow LAcb, \qquad LAab\ Abc \Rightarrow Aac,$$
$$Aca\ \ Abc \Rightarrow Aba;$$

$$LAab\ Aba \Rightarrow LAbb$$

reduces to:

*5.511 $LAab\ Aca\ Abc \Rightarrow LIac$.

*Case* 5.512. The consequent is $LIac$, and the antecedents include neither $LAaa$ nor $LAcc$ nor $Aac$, though they do include $Aca$. If (a) there is $LAb_ic$, or $Ib_ic$ and an $LAb_ia$-chain, or $Ib_ib_j$ and an $LAb_ia$- and an $Ab_jc$-chain, or $Ib_ib_j$ and an $Ab_ia$- and an $LAb_jc$-chain, then the expression is asserted. Otherwise (b) it is rejected.

*Proof*. (a) $LAb_ic$ and $Aca$ together yield $LIac$ (see Case 5.511). Secondly, we have $Ib_ic\ LAb_ia \Rightarrow LIac$ by Disamis $XLL$. Thirdly, we have $Ib_ib_j\ Ab_jc \Rightarrow Ib_ic$ by Darii $XXX$, and $Ib_ic\ LAb_ia \Rightarrow LIac$ by Disamis $XLL$. Fourthly, we have $Ib_ib_j\ Ab_ia \Rightarrow Ib_ja$ by Datisi $XXX$, and $Ib_ja\ LAb_jc \Rightarrow LIac$ by Datisi $LXL$.

(b) Put $b_i = d$ for all $LAb_ia$. We get no $Aad$ (since $Aab_i\ LAb_i\,a \Rightarrow LAaa$), nor $Idc$ (since $Ib_ic\ LAb_ia \Rightarrow LIac$). Put $b_i = g$ for all $Ab_ic$. No $Aag$ (since $Aab_i\ Ab_ic \Rightarrow Aac$), nor $LAga$ (none left), nor $LAgc$ (since no $LAb_ic$ present), nor $Igd$ (since $Ib_ib_j\ Ab_ic \Rightarrow Ib_jc$ and $Ib_jc\ LAb_ja \Rightarrow LIac$. I shall abbreviate this in future to "$Ib_ib_j\ Ab_ic \Rightarrow Ib_jc\ LAb_ja \Rightarrow LIac$"). Now identify all other variables with $b$. No $LAba$ nor $Abc$ (none left), nor $Abd$ (since $Ab_ib_j\ LAb_ja \Rightarrow LAb_ia$), nor $Abg$ (since $Ab_ib_j\ Ab_jc \Rightarrow Ab_ic$). This leaves:

(2) $LAbb\ LAdd\ LAgg\ LAab\ Aba\ MAac\ Aca\ MAad\ LAda\ MAag\ LIag\ Aga\ MAbc\ LAcb\ MAbd\ LAdb\ MAbg\ LAgb\ MAcd\ MAdc\ LAcg\ Agc\ MAdg\ MAgd\ \Rightarrow LIac$,
which, in virtue of the implications:

| | |
|---|---|
| $LAab\ Aba \Rightarrow LAbb$, | $LAab\ Aca \Rightarrow LAcb$, |
| $LAab\ LAda \Rightarrow LAdb$, | $LAab\ MAbc \Rightarrow MAac$, |
| $LAab\ MAbd \Rightarrow MAad$, | $Aca\ LAcg \Rightarrow LIag$, |
| $Aca\ Agc \Rightarrow Aga$, | $MAbc\ LAcg \Rightarrow MAbg$, |
| $LAcg\ Agc \Rightarrow LAgg$; | |
| $LAab\ Aga \Rightarrow LAgb$, | $LAab\ MAbg \Rightarrow MAag$, |
| $MAac\ LAda \Rightarrow MAdc$, | $LAda\ MAag \Rightarrow MAdg$, |
| $LAcb\ MAbd \Rightarrow MAcd$; | |
| $MAbd\ LAgb \Rightarrow MAgd$; | |

may be reduced to:

*5.512 $LAdd\ LAab\ Aba\ Aca\ LAda\ MAbc\ MAbd\ LAcg\ Agc \Rightarrow LIac$.

*Case* 5.513. The consequent is $LIac$, and the antecedents include neither $LAaa$ nor $LAcc$ nor $Aca$, though they do include $Aac$. Since $LIac$ and $LIca$ are equivalent, this case reduces to 5.512 with $a$ and $c$ interchanged. The same axiomatic rejection *5.512 will suffice for both cases.

*Case* 5.514. The consequent is $LIac$, and neither $LAaa$, $LAcc$, $Aac$ nor $Aca$ are present. If (a) there is $Iab_j$ and an $LAb_jc$-chain, or any other of the favourable conditions of Case 5.512 except the mere presence of $LAb_ic$ alone, the expression is asserted. Otherwise (b) it is rejected.

*Proof*. (a) $Iab_j\ LAb_jc \Rightarrow LIac$ by Darii $LXL$. For the other proofs see Case 5.512.

(b) Put $b_i = d$ for all $LAb_ia$. We get no $Aad$ (since $Aab_i\ LAb_ia \Rightarrow LAaa$), nor $Idc$ (since $Ib_ic\ LAb_ia \Rightarrow LIac$). Put $b_i = e$ for all $LAb_ic$. No $Iea$ (since $Ib_ia\ LAb_ic \Rightarrow LIac$), nor $Ace$ (since $Acb_i\ LAb_ic \Rightarrow LAcc$), nor $Ide$ (since $Ib_jb_i\ LAb_ja \Rightarrow LIab_i\ LAb_ic \Rightarrow LIac$ by Dimaris $LLL$). Put $b_i = h$ for all *pairs* of antecedents $Ab_ia$ and $Ab_ic$. No $LAha$ nor $LAhc$ (none left), nor $Aah$ (since $Aab_i\ Ab_ic \Rightarrow Aac$), nor $Ach$ (since $Acb_i\ Ab_ia \Rightarrow Aca$), nor $Ihd$ (since $Ib_ib_j\ Ab_ic \Rightarrow Ib_jc\ LAb_ja \Rightarrow LIac$), nor $Ihe$ (since $Ib_ib_j\ Ab_ja \Rightarrow Ib_ja\ LAb_jc \Rightarrow LIac$). Put $b_i = f$ for all other (non-paired) $Ab_ia$. No $LAfa$ (none left), nor $Afc$ (no pairs $Ab_ia\ Ab_ic$ left), nor $Acf$ (since $Acb_i\ Ab_ia \Rightarrow Aca$), nor $Afd$ (since $Ab_ib_j\ LAb_ja \Rightarrow LAb_ia$), nor $Ife$ (since $Ib_ib_j\ Ab_ia \Rightarrow Ib_ja\ LAb_jc \Rightarrow LIac$), nor $Afh$ (since $Ab_ib_j\ Ab_jc \Rightarrow Ab_ic$, and no pairs left). Put $b_i = g$ for all other (non-paired) $Ab_ic$. Similar arguments to those in the case of the variable $f$ will show that there results no $LAgc$, $Aga$, $Aag$, $Age$, $Igd$ nor $Agh$. We get no $Agf$ (since $Ab_ib_j\ Ab_ja \Rightarrow Ab_ia$), nor $Afg$ (since $Ab_jb_i\ Ab_ic \Rightarrow Ab_jc$). Finally, identify all other variables with $b$. We get no $Aba$ nor $Abc$ (none left), nor $Abd$ (since $Ab_ib_j\ LAb_ja \Rightarrow LAb_ia$), nor $Abe$ (since $Ab_ib_j\ LAb_jc \Rightarrow LAb_ic$), nor $Abf$ (since $Ab_ib_j\ Ab_ja \Rightarrow Ab_ia$), nor $Abg$ (since $Ab_ib_j\ Ab_jc \Rightarrow Ab_ic$), nor $Abh$ (since $Ab_ib_j\ Ab_ja \Rightarrow Ab_ia$). Writing the expression (2) so that, apart from the forms $LAbb$ etc., it is more or less symmetrical with regard to the pairs *a* and *c*, *d* and *e*, *f* and *g*, what we are left with is:

(2) $LAbb\ LAdd\ LAee\ LAff\ LAgg\ LAhh\ LAab\ MAba\ MAad\ LAda\ MAae\ MAea\ LAaf\ Afa\ MAag\ LIag\ MAga\ MAah\ LIah\ Aha\ MAbd\ LAdb\ MAbf\ LAfb\ LAdf\ MAfd\ MAdg\ MAgd\ MAdh\ MAhd\ MAfh\ LAhf\ MAde\ MAfg\ LIfg\ MAac\ Iac\ MAbh\ LAhb\ MAca\ MAgf\ MAed\ LAhg\ MAgf\ MAhe\ MAeh\ MAfe\ MAef\ MAge\ LAeg\ LAgb\ MAbg\ LAeb\ MAbe\ Ahc\ LIhc\ MAch\ MAfc\ LIfc\ MAcf\ Agc\ LAcg\ MAdc\ MAcd\ LAec\ MAce\ MAbc\ LAcb \Rightarrow LIac.$

I shall not list the implications required, but (2) is reducible to:

*5.514 $LAbb\ LAdd\ LAee\ LAhh\ LAab\ LAda\ LAaf\ Afa\ Aha\ MAbd\ MAbh\ MAbe\ Ahc\ Agc\ LAcg\ LAec\ LAcb \Rightarrow LIac.$

*Case* 5.52. The consequent is *LIac*, and either *LAaa* or *LAcc* (or both) is present. If (a) there is *Iac*, or $Iab_j$ and an $Ab_jc$-chain, or $Ib_ic$ and an $Ab_ia$-chain, or $Ib_ib_j$ and an $Ab_ia$- and an $Ab_jc$-chain, then the expression is asserted. Otherwise (b) it is rejected.

*Proof*. (a) We have $Iab_j\ Ab_jc \Rightarrow Iac$, $Ib_ic\ Ab_ia \Rightarrow Iac$, and $Ib_ib_j\ Ab_ia \Rightarrow Iab_j\ Ab_jc \Rightarrow Iac$. Because of the following theorems:

$LAcc\ Iac \Rightarrow LIac$ (substitution of Darii *LXL*)
$Iac\ LAaa \Rightarrow LIac$ ( „ „ Disamis *XLL*),

the combination of *Iac* and either *LAaa* or *LAcc* will always yield *LIac*.

(b) Put $b_i = a$ for all $Ab_ia$. This cannot produce *Iac* (since $Ib_ic\ Ab_ia \Rightarrow Iac\ LAaa\ (LAcc) \Rightarrow LIac$). Put $b_i = c$ for $Ab_ic$. No *Iac*, for similar reasons. Identify all other variables with *b*. No *Aba* nor *Abc* (none left). We thus have:

(2) $LAaa\ LAbb\ LAcc\ LAab\ MAba\ MAac\ MAca\ MAbc\ LAcb \Rightarrow LIac,$
which in virtue of the implications:

$LAab\ MAbc \Rightarrow MAac, \qquad MAba\ LAcb \Rightarrow MAca;$

reduces to:

*5.52 $LAaa\ LAbb\ LAcc\ LAab\ MAba\ MAbc\ LAcb \Rightarrow LIac.$

*Case* 5.6. The consequent is *Iac*. If (a) any of the favourable conditions of Case 5.52 holds, the expression is asserted. Otherwise (b) it is rejected.

*Proof.* (a) See Case 5.52.

(b) Proceed exactly as with Case 5.52. In the end we are left with:

*5.6 $LAaa\ LAbb\ LAcc\ LAab\ MAba\ MAbc\ LAcb \Rightarrow Iac$,

which suffices to reject *5.52. The latter is therefore superfluous.

*Case* 5.7. The consequent is $MIac$. If (a) there is either (1) $MIab_j$ and an $Ab_jc$-chain, or (2) $MIb_ic$ and an $Ab_ia$-chain, or (3) $Iab_j$ and an $MAb_jc$-chain, or (4) $Ib_ic$ and an $MAb_ia$-chain, or (5) $MIb_ib_j$ and an $Ab_ia$- and an $Ab_jc$-chain, or (6) $Ib_ib_j$ and an $Ab_ia$- and an $MAb_jc$-chain, or (7) $Ib_ib_j$ and an $MAb_ia$- and an $Ab_jc$-chain, then the expression is asserted. Otherwise (b) it is rejected.

*Proof.* (a) We have:

(1) $MIab_j\ Ab_jc \Rightarrow MIac$ (Darii $XMM$)
(2) $MIb_ic\ Ab_ia \Rightarrow MIac$ (Disamis $MXM$)
(3) $Iab_j\ MAb_jc \Rightarrow MIac$ (Darii $MXM$)
(4) $Ib_ic\ MAb_ia \Rightarrow MIac$ (Disamis $XMM$)
(5) $MIb_ib_j\ Ab_ia \Rightarrow MIab_j\ Ab_jc \Rightarrow MIac$
(6) $Ib_ib_j\ MAb_jc \Rightarrow MIb_ic\ Ab_ia \Rightarrow MIac$
(7) $Ib_ib_j\ MAb_ia \Rightarrow MIab_j\ Ab_jc \Rightarrow MIac$.

(b) Put $b_i = a$ for all $Ab_ia$. We get no $MIac$, since $MIb_ic\ Ab_ia \Rightarrow MIac$. Put $b_i = c$ for all $Ab_ic$. No $MIac$ for similar reasons. Put $b_i = f$ for all pairs $Ib_ia$ and $Ib_ic$. No $MAfa$ (since $MAb_ia\ Ib_ic \Rightarrow MIac$), nor $MAfc$ (since $MAb_ic\ Ib_ia \Rightarrow MIac$). Put $b_i = d$ for all remaining $Ib_ia$. No $Ada$ (none left), nor $MAdc$ (since $MAb_ic\ Ib_ia \Rightarrow MIac$), nor $Idc$ (since all pairs $Ib_ia\ Ib_ic$ gone), nor $Afd$ (since $Ab_jb_i\ Ib_jc \Rightarrow Ib_ic$, and all pairs gone). Put $b_i = e$ for all remaining $Ib_ic$. As in the case of $d$, there results no $Aec$, $MAea$, $Iea$, nor $Afe$. Further, we get no $Ade$ (since $Ab_jb_i\ Ib_ja \Rightarrow Ib_ia$), nor $Aed$ (since $Ab_ib_j\ Ib_ic \Rightarrow Ib_jc$). Finally, identify all other variables with $b$. We get no $Iba$ nor $Ibc$ (none left), nor $Adb$ (since $Ab_jb_i\ Ib_ja \Rightarrow Ib_ia$), nor $Aeb$ (since $Ab_jb_i\ Ib_jc \Rightarrow Ib_ic$), nor $Afb$ (since $Ab_jb_i\ Ib_ja \Rightarrow Ib_ia$). This leaves us with:

(2) $LAaa\ LAbb\ LAcc\ LAdd\ LAee\ LAff\ MAab\ MAba\ LAad\ MAda\ MAae\ LAaf\ LAbd\ MAdb\ LAdf\ MAfd\ MAde\ LIde\ LAbf$

*MAfb MAed MAfe LAef MAeb LAbe LAcf MAcd LAec LAce MAcb MAbc* ⇒ *MIac*,

once again an expression symmetrical with respect to *a* and *c*, *d* and *e*. In virtue of the following implications:

| | |
|---|---|
| *LAad LAdf* ⇒ *LAaf*, | *MAda LAbd* ⇒ *MAba*, |
| *LAbd LAdf* ⇒ *LAbf*, | *LAbd MAfb* ⇒ *MAfd*, |
| *LAbd LAbe* ⇒ *LIde*, | *LAdf MAfb* ⇒ *MAdb*, |
| *MAfb LAef* ⇒ *MAeb*, | *MAfb LAbe* ⇒ *MAfe*, |
| *LAef LAce* ⇒ *LAcf*, | *LAbe MAec* ⇒ *MAbc*; |
| *LAad MAdb* ⇒ *MAab*, | *LAaf MAfe* ⇒ *MAae*, |
| *LAbd MAeb* ⇒ *MAed*, | *MAdb LAbe* ⇒ *MAde*, |
| *MAfd LAcf* ⇒ *MAcd*, | *MAfb LAcf* ⇒ *MAcb*; |

we may reduce (2) to:

*5.7 *LAaa LAbb LAcc LAdd LAee LAff LAad MAda LAbd LAdf MAfb LAef LAbe MAec LAce* ⇒ *MIac*.

It remains now to collect the rejected expressions *5.12, *5.21, *5.3, *5.41, *5.42, *5.511, *5.512, *5.514, *5.6 and *5.7, renumber them as axiomatic rejections *9 to *18 respectively, and add them to axiomatic rejections *1 and *2. With this our decision procedure for the *L–X–M* calculus of modal syllogistic is complete.

## CHAPTER IV

# THE CONTINGENT MOODS

## 22. General remarks. The contingency operator

It is time now to take up an extremely important and difficult subject: the meaning which Aristotle attaches to the word "possibly". We should rather speak of "meanings", for it is well known that Aristotle explicitly recognized two senses of the word. The germ of his distinction between the two meanings is to be found in *De Interpretatione*, 22b10–23a18. It would seem, Aristotle says, that when something is necessary it is also possible. For it it did not follow that it were possible, the opposite would follow, namely that it were impossible (here Aristotle makes use of the law *CNCpqCpNq* of the propositional calculus), and in that case what is necessary would be impossible, which is absurd (22b14). But there is another argument which seems to show the opposite; that what is necessary cannot also be possible. For it might be said that something which is possibly something else is also possibly not that thing – that what may be may also not be (22b33). In this sense what is necessary would be incompatible with what is possible, for it is not permitted for something which necessarily is, possibly not to be. Possibility seems to be both implied and excluded by necessity.

Aristotle's way of resolving this dilemma is to distinguish two species of possibility. In *An. pr.* 25a37–39 he says that the word ἐνδεχόμενον ("possible") is used in several ways, for we say that what is necessary and that what is not necessary and that τὸ δυνατόν (see below) are all possible. Ross points out (p. 295) that these are plainly not three *senses* of "possible", but three kinds of case in which the word can be applied. Later, in 32a18–20, Aristotle explicitly states that by "possible" he means that which is not necessary but the supposition of which involves nothing impossible (ἀδύνατον). This amounts to saying that the possible is that which is neither necessary nor impossible. When Aristotle uses the word ἐνδεχόμενον in this sense I shall follow Ross's translation of it as "contingent" (see Ross, p. 296). The remaining sense (in which what is possible can also be necessary, and in which ἐνδεχόμενον means simply "not impossible") is covered by the word δυνατόν, or "possible".

It is interesting to trace the subsequent history of Aristotle's distinction. Łukasiewicz (p. 154) credits A. Becker with having first pointed out the ambiguity of ἐνδεχόμενον. But as Becker himself says in another work, this ambiguity was known to Boethius, to whom, or to whose predecessor Marius Victorinus, we are indebted for the use of the Latin *contingere* as a translation of ἐνδέχεσθαι [1]. In fact Boethius seems to have used *contingere* in no less than three senses, namely, (i) in the sense of "to happen" or "to occur" (*accidere, evenire*, συμβαίνειν), (ii) in the sense of "to be possible", where there is no question of excluding "to be necessary" (*posse*, δύνασθαι, ἐνδέχεσθαι), and (iii) in the sense of "to be possible" which *does* exclude "to be necessary" (ἐνδέχεσθαι) [2]. If we divide the class of all propositions in the following manner:

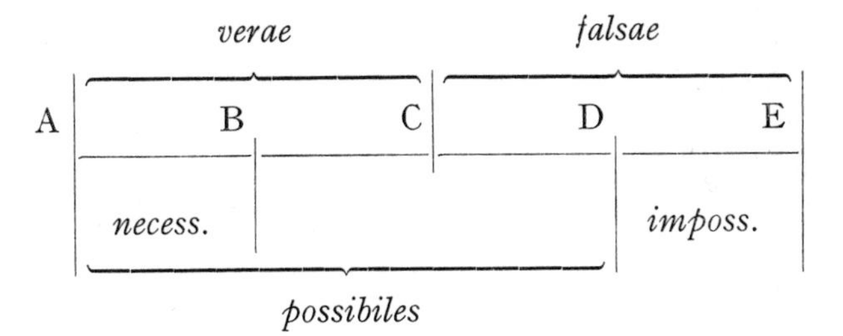


[1] A. Becker, *Die Vorgeschichte des philosophischen Terminus "contingens"* (VTC), Heidelberg, 1938. We also owe to Boethius the term *modus*, which he used to translate Ammonius' τρόπος (Bochenski, NHPM, p. 683).

[2] For (i) and (ii) see Becker, VTC, p. 17, and for (iii) p. 33.

then contingent propositions in the sense of

(i) will fall within the segment AC
(ii) will fall within the segment AD
(iii) will fall within the segment BD [1].

In *An. pr.* 32b4–23 Aristotle further subdivides the contingent into (a) that which happens generally or usually (without of course being necessary), such as a man's turning grey, and (b) that which happens fortuitously or accidentally, such as an earthquake's occurring while someone is walking. The scholastic term for (a) was *contingens natum;* for (b) *contingens ad utrumlibet* [2]. Although Aristotle says that syllogisms are generally made about the former rather than the latter, he never makes any *formal* distinction between the two: this was left to successors such as Albert the Great, who upheld the legitimacy of complementary conversion (see sect. 23) for *contingens ad utrumlibet* only [3]. Averroes expanded Aristotle's twofold division into a threefold one, distinguishing possibility *in plus* (e.g. that a boy should attain puberty), *in minus* (e.g. that a boy should not attain puberty), and *in aequalitatem* (e.g. that this cloak should be torn or not be torn) [4].

Recent times have seen a renewal of interest in the Aristotelian concept of contingency, namely contingency in sense (iii) above. We find in Hugh MacColl's work the attempt to define a formal operator $\theta$ such that the symbol $\phi^\theta$ stands for the assertion that the proposition $\phi$ is *neither certain nor impossible.* It is, in MacColl's terminology, a *variable* proposition [5]. If we identify "certain" with "necessary" we arrive precisely at Aristotle's concept of contingency. One of MacColl's results is that, while any two certain (necessary) propositions, or, for that matter, any two impossible propositions, are equivalent in the sense of implying one another, the same is not in general true of variable (contingent) propositions.

---

1 Becker, VTC, p. 34. (iii) is sometimes distinguished from (ii) as "two-sided" as opposed to "one-sided" possibility.

2 Bochenski, NHPM, p. 677.

3 Bochenski, NHPM, p. 685.

4 Averroes, *fol.* 36$^r$.

5 H. MacColl, *Symbolic Logic and Its Applications*, London 1906, pp. 6, 10.

Another apparent feature of contingency is that if any proposition is contingent, then so is its negation. This property is to be found explicitly stated by Becker [1]. Using Prior's $Q$ as the contingency operator in place of Becker's $E_2$, we have, corresponding to Aristotle's definition:

$$EQpKNLpNLNp,$$

from which we get, using the definition of $M$:

$$EQpKMNpMp.$$

Now, substituting $Np$ for $p$ and cancelling double negations:

$$EQNpKMpMNp$$

from which:

$$EQpQNp.$$

This consequence of the definition of contingency as that which is neither necessary nor impossible did not apparently disturb Aristotle; in fact it seems quite in line with his statement in 32a32 that "it is contingent to belong" is convertible into "it is contingent not to belong". It did however disturb Łukasiewicz, who in 1930 showed that if the law $EQpQNp$ is combined with Leśniewski's law $C\delta pC\delta Np\delta q$ governing truth-functions, the result is $CQpQq$, namely that if any proposition is contingent then every proposition is contingent [2]. To avoid this paradoxical consequence, Łukasiewicz has constructed an elaborate modal logic containing not one but two "twin" contingency operators. However, his system is quite un-Aristotelian, as may be seen from the fact that it does not allow either for complementary conversion of contingent premisses, or for moods with contingent conclusions [3]. Hence we shall pursue a different tack. To avoid paradox, either we may deny that Leśniewski's law $C\delta pC\delta Np\delta q$ applies to $Q$ (see Prior pp. 191–3),

[1] Becker, ATM, p. 14.

[2] Łukasiewicz, § 4 of *Philosophische Bemerkungen zu mehrwertigen Systemen des Aussagenkalküls*, Comptes rendus de la Société des Sciences et des Lettres de Varsovie, Cl. III, 23 (1930), pp. 51–77. See also Prior, p. 191.

[3] Łukasiewicz, pp. 201–2. For a detailed criticism of Lukasiewicz's concept of contingency, see the author's review of the second edition of *Aristotle's Syllogistic*, forthcoming in vol. 27 no. 2 of The Journal of Symbolic Logic.

or we may deny that the law *EQpQNp* is Aristotelian in the first place. The second of these alternatives is the one we shall adopt [1].

## 23. Conversion and opposition of contingent premisses

Aristotle discusses the conversion of contingent premisses in three places. In chapter 3 of the *Prior Analytics* we read that contingent premisses which are affirmative convert precisely as affirmative assertorics; thus *QAab* converts *per accidens*, and *QIab* simpliciter, to *QIba*. But the case of the negatives is different. The universal negative *QEab* does not convert, while the particular negative *QOab* does. Aristotle makes an attempt to explain this odd result by remarking that these seemingly negative contingent propositions are really affirmative in form, and therefore in conversion will behave like affirmatives (25b19–25). That is, *QEab* will convert *per accidens*, and *QOab simpliciter*.

In chapter 13 we learn why *QEab* and *QOab* are really affirmative in form. The reason is, that *QEab* is convertible with *QAab*, and *QOab* with *QIab*. Ross's translation of 32a29–38 reads thus [2]:

"It follows that problematic [i.e. contingent] propositions are convertible – not the affirmative with the negative, but propositions affirmative in form are convertible in respect of the opposition between the two things that are said to be possible, i.e. "it is capable of belonging" into "it is capable of not belonging", "it is capable of belonging to every instance" into "it is capable of belonging to no instance", and into "it is capable of not belonging to every instance", "it is capable of belonging to some instance" into "it is capable of not belonging to some instance"; and so on. ... For since the contingent is not necessary, and that which is not necessary is capable of not existing, if it is contingent for *A* to belong to *B* it is also contingent for it not to belong".

When Aristotle speaks of "conversion" here, he evidently means

---

[1] The author has recently learned that an axiomatization of Lewis's modal system S5, with *Q* primitive instead of *L* or *M*, was made by Lemmon and Gjertsen in 1959. Those interested in contingency logic may find the axioms required in Prior (2nd edition), p. 312.

[2] Ross, p. 326.

something different from ordinary conversion. Following Ross, I shall refer to the mutual convertibility of *QAab* and *QEab*, and of *QIab* and *QOab*, as "complementary conversion" [1]. It should be noted that the passage quoted above does not allow the conversion of *QAab* into *QOab* to be mutual; *QAab* implies *QOab* but not *vice versa*. The following, adapted from Becker, is a schematic representation of the various relations of complementary conversion recognized by Aristotle [2]:

TABLE 9

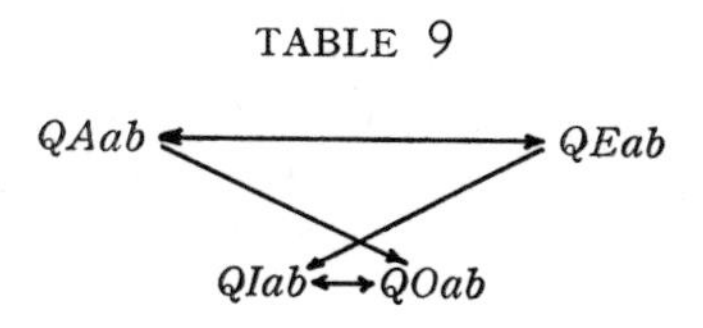


A clear view of the differences between Aristotle's conceptions of contingency and possibility may be obtained by comparing table 9 with table 6 in sect. 13. More will be said about complementary conversion later.

In chapter 17, having discussed complementary conversion, Aristotle returns to the (ordinary) inconvertibility of *QEab*. There, in 36b35–37a3, Aristotle gives what is in essence the following argument. We know that *QAab* implies *QEab*, and that *QEba* implies *QAba*. Therefore, if *QEab* implied *QEba*, *QAab* would imply *QAba*, which it does not. Hence *QEab* is not convertible. For more on this inconvertibility see sect. 28.

We must now discuss those relations which hold between contingent premisses on the one hand and necessary and possible premisses on the other. Let us consider the "octagon of opposition" of table 6. In order for *LAab* and *MOab* to be contradictories, the following implications must hold:

(1) *C LAab NMOab*, i.e. *C LNOab NMOab*
and (2) *C NLAab MOab*, i.e. *C NLNOab MOab*

But when we come to consider the notion of contingency in place

[1] Ross, p. 298.

[2] Becker, ATM, p. 21. Table 9 lacks the relations of subalternation found in Becker, for which see sect. 27.

of the notion of possibility, only implication (1), and not (2), holds. Replacing $M$ by $Q$, (1) becomes "If it is impossible that some $A$ is not $B$, then it is not contingent that some $A$ is not $B$", which accords with Aristotle's meaning of contingency. On the other hand (2) becomes "If it is not impossible that some $A$ is not $B$, then it is contingent that some $A$ is not $B$", which is false, since that which is not impossible may be either contingent or necessary. In symbols,

(3) $C\ LAab\ NQOab$,

while the implication $C\ NLAab\ QOab$ fails. That is to say, $LAab$ and $QOab$ are contraries rather than contradictories. The same holds when we substitute $Q$ for $M$ in the other pairs of contradictories in table 6.

We now note that (3) is equivalent to

(4) $C\ QOab\ NLAab$,
i.e. to (5) $C\ QOab\ MOab$.

Hence implications of type (5) may be taken to stand for the relations of opposition, namely relations of contrariety, extending between necessary and contingent premisses. The sum total of the information contained in tables 6 and 9 may be condensed into the following comprehensive table, where the wavy lines, joining sub-contraries, replace the laws of modal subordination $C\ LAab\ MAab$ etc.:

TABLE 10

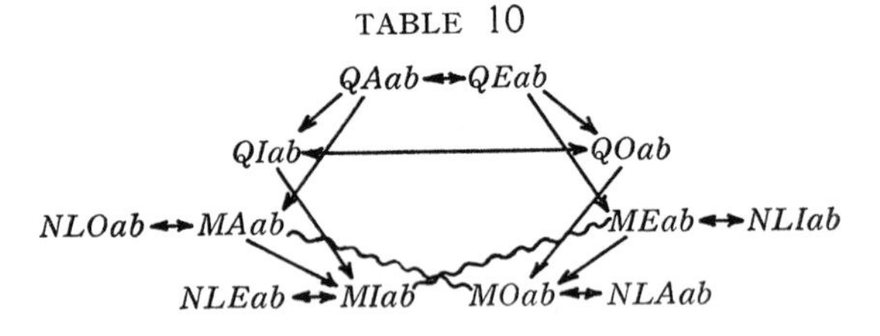


## 24. Can contingency be defined in terms of possibility and necessity?

Aristotle's stipulation of the contingent as that which is "not necessary, but the supposition of which involves nothing impossible" makes it tempting to define $Qp$ as $KNLpNLNp$, i.e. as $KMpMNp$.

Definition of the various $Q$-premisses along these lines would result in the following:

$$QAab = K\,MAab\,MOab \qquad \text{Df } Q1$$
$$QEab = K\,MEab\,MIab \qquad \text{Df } Q2$$
$$QIab = K\,MIab\,MEab \qquad \text{Df } Q3$$
$$QOab = K\,MOab\,MAab \qquad \text{Df } Q4$$ [1].

In general, as shown in sect. 22, this definition of $Qp$ leads to the equivalence $EQpQNp$. But there are three things wrong with definitions $Q1$–4.

(i) They permit the implication $C\,QOab\,QAab$, which Aristotle rejects.

(ii) They do not permit the implications $C\,QAab\,QEab$ and $C\,QIab\,QOab$, which Aristotle accepts.

(iii) They permit the convertibility of $QEab$ (through the convertibility of $MEab$ and $MIab$), which Aristotle rejects.

Definitions $Q1$–4 must therefore be discarded. Might it not, however, be possible to change them so as to conform to Aristotle's intentions more closely? The following definitions, for example:

$$QAab = QEab = K\,MAab\,MEab \qquad \text{Df } Q5$$
$$QIab = QOab = K\,MIab\,MEab \qquad \text{Df } Q6$$

preserve all the Aristotelian laws of opposition, subalternation, complementary and ordinary conversion. However, they have other short-comings which appear only when we consider contingent syllogisms. For example, in *An. pr.* chapter 14 Aristotle states that "it is clear from the definition" of contingency that Barbara $QQQ$ is valid. Yet, using definition $Q5$ of $QAab$, we get for Barbara $QQQ$:

$$CKKK\,MAbc\,MEbc\,MAab\,MEab\,K\,MAac\,MEac,$$

and *this* formula is rejected, not asserted, in the $L$–$X$–$M$ calculus. In fact, since no $MMM$ mood is asserted in that calculus, no $QQQ$ mood is provable in it using definitions $Q5$–6.

---

[1] To judge from Bochenski's summary of Pseudo-Scotus' system of laws governing contingent premisses when the latter are taken *in sensu composito* (Bochenski, NHPM, p. 689), Pseudo-Scotus must have relied precisely on definitions $Q1$–4.

Another attempt to define Aristotle's notion of contingency in terms of simpler concepts might be made by pursuing the following train of thought [1]. If we take the ordinary universal assertoric premiss in the form Aristotle writes it, i.e. "*A* belongs to all *B*", or "*A* is predicated of all *B*", then we are free to say that a necessary premiss involves both actual predication and the necessity of predication, whereas a possible premiss involves only the possibility of predication without implying actual predication. A contingent premiss, however, could be taken to involve actual predication while at the same time denying necessity of predication. Under this interpretation, "it is contingent for a man's hair to go grey" would mean "a man's hair goes grey, but it is possible for it not to go grey", or in formal terms:

$$QAab = K\,Aab\,MOab \qquad \text{Df } Q7$$
$$QEab = K\,Eab\,MIab \qquad \text{Df } Q8$$
$$\text{etc.}$$

Unfortunately, however, these definitions will not allow us to assert Barbara *QQQ* either. The latter becomes

$$CKKK\,Abc\,MObc\,Aab\,MOab\,K\,Aac\,MOac,$$

namely a rejected formula. So this attempt at defining *Q* breaks down also.

If, however, we lay down purely arbitrary definitions of *Q*-premisses, without any intuitive justification but solely in the interests of validating contingent syllogisms, we shall be able to reproduce Aristotle's system with a moderate degree of accuracy. The definitions which produce the best results are as follows:

$$QAab = QEab = K\,Aab\,Eab \qquad \text{Df } Q9$$
$$QIab = QOab = K\,Iab\;\;Oab \qquad \text{Df } Q10.$$

It will be noted that these definitions satisfy all the logical relations

---

[1] I owe the germ of this reasoning to some remarks in Venant Cauchy's "Notes on the Modal Syllogism", *The Modern Schoolman*, January 1957, pp. 121–30.

of table 10. They do not, on the other hand, allow for the convertibility of *QIab* or *QOab*, and they permit the entailment by a contingent proposition of the corresponding assertoric. Apart from these un-Aristotelian features, however, the definitions lead to useful results. Barbara *QQQ*, for example, becomes

*CKKK Abc Ebc Aab Eab K Aac Eac*,

which is asserted in the *L–X–M* calculus in virtue of Barbara and Celarent *XXX*. Cesare *QQQ*, on the other hand,

*CKKK Acb Ecb Aab Eab K Aac Eac*,

is neither asserted in the *L–X–M* calculus nor held to be valid by Aristotle. But the fit between the two systems is far from perfect. Disamis *QXQ*, for example, is asserted in the *L–X–M* calculus but rejected by Aristotle. In view of this and other divergencies which I shall detail later in sect. 37, there would seem to be a good case for giving up the attempt to define Aristotle's concept of contingency in terms of other notions, and instead to try to reconstruct Aristotle's system of contingent syllogisms using a logical operator *Q* that is primitive.

## 25. Axiomatization of the contingent moods. The *Q-L-X-M* calculus

In this section the *L–X–M* calculus of sect. 14 will be expanded into a *Q–L–X–M* calculus by the addition of axioms from which a collection of theorems all containing the undefined operator *Q* is deducible. These *Q*-theorems will enter into logical relations with pure *L–X–M* theorems in virtue of the following four implications of table 10:

*C QAab MAab*
*C QEab MEab*
*C QIab MIab*
*C QOab MOab*.

In order to convey the complexity of the network of interrelations of syllogistic moods with contingent, necessary, assertoric and possible premisses and conclusion I give below a table similar to table 8, p. 45, but lacking relations of equivalence [1].

TABLE 11

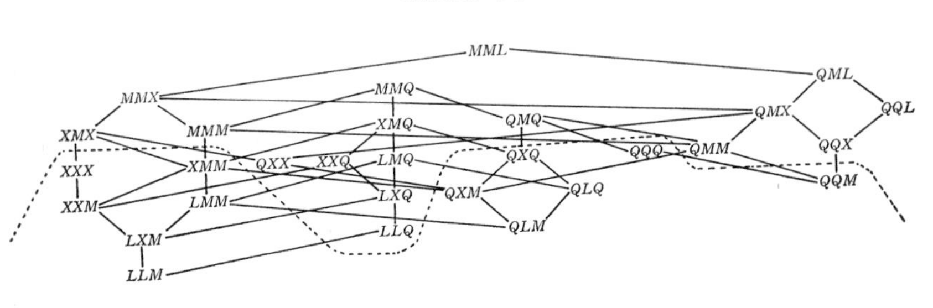


Syllogistic types below the dotted line either contain some moods recognised as valid by Aristotle, or contain moods which are entailed by such moods.

We may now proceed to the axiomatization of the *Q–L–X–M* system. This is accomplished by adding to the basis of the *L–X–M* system the primitive monadic function *Q*, with rules of formation governing its use exactly similar to those for the function *L*. In addition certain axioms are added, as detailed below. However, one small change must first be made in the *L–X–M* axioms. If we retain the axiom *LIaa*, we may, by means of the substitution *CK QAac LIaa Iac* of Darii *QLX* (proved below), derive the implication *C QAac Iac*, which is un-Aristotelian. The axiom *LIaa* was added to the *L–X–M* calculus in the interests of simplifying the decision procedure. Since I shall not construct a decision procedure for the *Q–L–X–M* calculus, we may replace in it the axiom *LIaa* by Łukasiewicz's original axiom *Iaa*.

---

[1] There are, in addition to the 8 equivalences of table 8, only 3 "*reductio*" equivalences among contingent syllogistic moods, namely $QMX \leftrightarrow QXL$, $QMM \leftrightarrow QLL$, and $QXM \leftrightarrow QLX$, to raise the number of syllogistic types in table 11 from 29 to 40. Counting syllogisms with permuted premisses separately we get 64, the number of possible forms of *Q–L–X–M* syllogism.

*Axioms*

Seven syllogistic moods:

| | | |
|---|---|---|
| 200. | *CK QAbc QAab QAac* | (Barbara *QQQ*) |
| 201. | *CK QAbc QIab QIac* | (Darii *QQQ*) |
| 202. | *CK QAbc Aab QEac* | (*QXQ–AAE* in the first figure) |
| 203. | *CK QAbc Iab QIac* | (Darii *QXQ*) |
| 204. | *CK Abc QAab MAac* | (Barbara *XQM*) |
| 205. | *CK Ebc QAab MEac* | (Celarent *XQM*) |
| 206. | *CK Ebc QIab MOac* | (Ferio *XQM*), |

plus three entailments establishing complementary conversion:

207. *C QEab QAab*
208. *C QIab QOab*
209. *C QOab QIab*,

plus a law of ordinary conversion:

210. *C QIab QIba*,

plus three laws of modal subordination:

211. *C QEab MEab*
212. *C QIab MIab*
213. *C QOab MOab*.

From these axioms, as will be shown, we may prove all the contingent syllogistic moods held to be valid by Aristotle, together, unfortunately, with some which he held to be invalid. In what follows, I shall first prove the various laws of complementary conversion, subalternation, ordinary conversion and modal subordination. I shall then discuss each of the main groups of contingent moods, showing agreements and discrepancies between the *Q–L–X–M* and Aristotle's system. Finally, for interest's sake, I shall compare the agreement or "Aristotelicity" of moods deduced in the *Q–L–X–M* system with the agreement of contingent moods provable in the *L–X–M* system using the definitions *Q*9 and *Q*10.

## 26. The laws of complementary conversion

IV=$CI$–$CII$–$C$202–214. $C\ Aab\ C\ QAbc\ QEac$
214=$C$1–215. $C\ QAab\ QEab$

Theses 207 and 215 together constitute the law of complementary conversion of universal contingent premisses. The corresponding law for particular premisses is given by 208 and 209. These laws have already been discussed in sect. 23, and we shall now inquire more closely into the details of Aristotle's use of them.

In general, it is probable that when he establishes that two propositions admit of simple, not *per accidens* "conversion", Aristotle means that one may be replaced by the other in all instances as equivalent to it (though see Ross, p. 293, where six usages of ἀντιστρέφειν in the *Analytics* are distinguished). The matter is complex, however. When he first makes use of complementary conversion in 33a5–11 Aristotle says, "But whenever *A* may belong to all *B*, and *B* may belong to no *C*, then indeed no syllogism results from the premisses assumed, but if the premiss *BC* is converted after the manner of problematic propositions, the same syllogism results as before. For since it is possible that *B* should belong to no *C*, it is possible also that it should belong to all *C*". Here Aristotle is saying that we may reduce the contingent mood *AEA* in the first figure to the valid Barbara *QQQ* if we replace the minor premiss *QEab* of the former by its complementary converse *QAab*. This operation of replacing a *QE*-premiss in a mood to be demonstrated by a *QA*-premiss, thus obtaining a mood already proven, is repeated by him on 12 separate occasions [1]. We find similar replacements of a *QO*-premiss by a *QI*-premiss on 5 occasions, as for example in 33a27–34 when he proves the mood *AOI* in the first figure from Darii *QQQ*. In all these cases it is a *negative* premiss in the mood to be demonstrated which is converted, the result being a proven mood whose corresponding premiss is affirmative. Strangely, Aristotle never reverses this procedure to demonstrate a mood by converting an *affirmative* premiss, as for example one might think he could have done in order to prove the

[1] See Becker, ATM p. 22, for references to the passages in question.

mood *AAE* in the first figure [1] from the valid Celarent *QQQ*. Nor do we ever find him bringing complementary conversion to bear upon the *conclusion* of a syllogism, as he might have done to prove the mood *AIO* in the first figure from Darii *QQQ*. Why? Might it be that Aristotle did not regard the pairs *QAab* and *QEab*, *QIab* and *QOab* as completely interchangeable equivalents after all?

I think that in fact he *did* regard complementary converses as equivalent, and that his apparent preference for converting negative to the exclusion of affirmative contingent premisses is capable of a different interpretation. In order to see this, let us write down the eight possible first figure moods with universal premisses and conclusion [2].

200. *AAA* Barbara *QQQ*
300. *EAE* Celarent *QQQ*
489. *AEA* reduced to *AAA* by complementary conversion of minor (33a5)
490. *EEA* reduced to *AAA* by complementary conversion of major and minor (33a13)
491. *AAE*
492. *EAA*
493. *AEE*
494. *EEE*
} not mentioned by Aristotle

Once we set out the moods in this way, it is possible to give a plausible explanation of why Aristotle does not mention the moods 491–494. It is, I think, because each of them may be derived from 200, 300, 489 and 490 respectively by complementary conversion of the conclusion. Aristotle never uses complementary conversion on the conclusion of a syllogism. This is not to say that

[1] This mood is mentioned neither by him nor by Becker or Ross, who set out to complete Aristotle's work by listing some syllogistic moods validated by complementary conversion which Aristotle omits (Becker, ATM, p. 75, Ross, facing p. 286). It is significant that Ross speaks of moods validated by complementary conversion of *negative* premisses only.

[2] Moods provable from the axioms are numbered consecutively, beginning at 300, with moods provable by complementary conversion coming at the end. See table 13, page 92.

he regarded the operation as invalid, but probably only that he was interested more in what combinations of premisses will yield a conclusion than in what conclusion a given combination will yield. Mood 492, for example, could have been easily reduced to 200 by complementary conversion of the major, but Aristotle, having already dealt with the combination of premisses *EA* in Celarent *QQQ*, may well have refrained from pursuing the matter any further, judging it obvious in view of what had been said that if the conclusion *QEab* could be drawn, then so could the conclusion *QAab*. If this interpretation be correct, the fact that Aristotle never proves a mood by taking the complementary converse of an *affirmative* premiss does not mean that he did not regard such premisses as interchangeable with their negative opposites, nor that he would prefer us to interpret complementary conversion as one-way implication rather than as equivalence, but only that he could deal with all possible combinations of contingent premisses by converting the negative ones alone. If any further reason be needed for taking complementary converses as genuine equivalents, it may be noted that Aristotle's argument in 36b35–37a3 for the inconvertibility of *QEab* requires both that the latter implies and is implied by *QAab*.

## 27. The laws of subalternation

IV=*C*I–*C*II–*C*203–216. *C Iab C QAbc QIac*

216=*C*15–217. *C QAab QIab*

(law of subalternation of *QI*-premiss)

IV=*C*207–*C*217–218. *C QEab QIab*

IV=*C*218–*C*208–219. *C QEab QOab*

(law of subalternation of *QO*-premiss)

These laws are not explicitly stated by Aristotle, but are necessary consequences both of (a) the laws of complementary conversion stated in 32a29–38, and (b) the laws of conversion per accidens of *QAab* and *QEab*, together with the laws of simple conversion of *QIab* and *QOab* (see below). They are, however, logically simpler than the laws of conversion *per accidens*, and hence are used in the *Q–L–X–M* system for the proof of the latter rather than *vice versa*.

## 28. The laws of ordinary conversion

210. *C QIab QIba*

(law of conversion of *QI*-premiss)

IV=*C*209–*C*210–220. *C QOab QIba*

IV=*C*220–*C*208–221. *C QOab QOba*

(law of conversion of *QO*-premiss)

IV=*C*217–*C*210–222. *C QAab QIba*

(law of conversion of *QA*-premiss)

IV=*C*219–*C*221–223. *C QEab QOba*

(law of conversion of *QE*-premiss)

These laws have been discussed in sect. 23. Although there may seem to be no clear formulation in *An. pr.* of the law of conversion *per accidens* of the *QE*-premiss, we have Aristotle's statement in 25b25 that "in conversion [contingent negative] premisses will behave like the other affirmative propositions". Furthermore this convertibility cannot be denied once we accept complementary conversion and the conversion *per accidens* of the *QA*-premiss.

The inconvertibility of *QEab* was one of the things about Aristotle's system that scandalized Theophrastus. Alexander twice attributes the thesis *C QEab QEba* to him, the argument being as follows:

"If it is possible for *A* to belong to no *B*, then it is possible for *B* to belong to no *A*. For since it is possible for *A* to belong to no *B*, then, when it does not belong to any, it is possible for *A* to be separated from all of the *B*'s. In this case *B* will be separated from *A*" [1].

That this argument was not considered by Alexander to be a valid refutation of Aristotle's thesis is pointed out by Rondelet [2]. Though it doubtless results, he says, that *B* is separated from every *A*, it does not follow that it is separated in a *contingent* manner, as is required by the argument. In fact, nothing prevents part of *B* from being separated from *A necessarily*, and part contingently. Hence the refutation fails.

---

[1] Translated by M. Kneale, p. 102.

[2] A. Rondelet, *Théorie logique des propositions modales*, Paris 1861, p. 166.

Whatever its merits, however, we see once more in this notion of separability the influence of the Theophrastean spatial analogy which was discussed in sect. 6. From the fact that Theophrastus defended the convertibility of *QEab*, that he rejected complementary conversion, and that he took the negation of *QEab* to be *LIab* [1], we deduce that he entirely did away with the Aristotelian concept of contingency, substituting for it the logically simpler concept of one-sided possibility.

In modern times, Theophrastus' doctrine of the convertibility of *QEab* has found support from Łukasiewicz (p. 194 ff.) and from Mrs. Kneale (p. 87). The latter's argument is of interest. Aristotle says (37a5–8) that while it is contingent that no man should be white, we cannot infer that it is similarly contingent that no white thing should be a man, for many white things are *necessarily* not men – e.g. (Alexander) snow and swans. But, as Mrs. Kneale rightly says, if the converted proposition is false because snow and swans exist, the original proposition should be false because negroes exist. Hence Aristotle's attempted proof is weak. The inconvertibility of *QEab* has not as yet, I think, found any modern defenders.

## 29. The laws of modal subordination

204=*C*1–224. *C QAab MAab*

Theorem 224 is the law of modal subordination of the *QA*-premiss. The other laws of modal subordination are laid down as axioms. Once again, Aristotle never states these laws explicitly. But he makes frequent implicit use of them in the form of a relation of opposition amounting to contrariety between contingent and necessary premisses. In 37a24–26 we find a statement of the opposition of *LIab* and *QEab* which we may write as *C QEab NLIab*, i.e. as *C QEab MEab*. Again, this opposition frequently occurs in *reductio* proofs of contingent moods. For example, in proving Celarent *LQX* in 36a7–15 Aristotle makes use of the *reductio* mood

---

[1] Bochenski, LT, pp. 74–5.

Ferio *LXL* [1], whose conclusion, *LOcb*, must be taken as contrary to the premiss *QAcb* of Celarent *LQX*. We conclude that Aristotle makes implicit use of the laws of modal subordination.

## 30. Conspectus of Aristotle's contingent moods

All the logical relations involving the operator *Q* in table 10, plus the laws of ordinary conversion, have now been proved in the *Q–L–X–M* system. It remains to consider inferences from two premisses, namely contingent syllogisms, and in discussing the different categories of them separately, it will be useful to refer to a conspective presentation of those which Aristotle held to be valid or invalid. In table 12 (overleaf) Aristotle's method of proof is indicated for valid moods; moods explicitly held to be invalid by him are in bold face, with references to the first lines of relevant passages in *An. pr.;* moods not mentioned by him are left blank. Apart from moods which are provable by modal subordination from other moods, and which occur in ordinary face, there is no doubt that Aristotle intended these unmentioned moods to be considered invalid. As will be noted, he tires of matters of invalidity when he comes to discuss the third figure. In my notes accompanying table 12, I accordingly discuss in detail only the first figure: the blanks in the other two figures may be filled in similarly. As was the case with table 1, table 12 is intended to supplement Becker's table (ATM, facing p. 88) and Ross's table (facing p. 286).

[1] He could have used Festino *LXL* directly, but instead converted the major premiss.

NOTES TO TABLE 12

| | | |
|---|---|---|
| C. | – | reduce by conversion, |
| C.c. | – | reduce by complementary conversion, |
| R. | – | reduce by *reductio ad absurdum*, |
| M.s. | – | derive by modal subordination. |

*Mood no.*

13 This mood, which is not to be found in Becker, is discussed by Aristotle only under a general rubric of third figure *QQQ*

(notes continued on p. 86)

TABLE 12

| | *QQQ* | *QXQ* | *XQQ* | *QXM* | *XQM* | *QLQ* |
|---|---|---|---|---|---|---|
| Barbara | 1 Perfect | 15 Perfect | **29** | 43 | 57 R. to Bocardo LXX | 71 Perfect |
| Celarent | 2 ,, | 16 ,, | **30** (34b32) | 44 | 58 R. to Disamis LXX | 72 ,, |
| Darii | 3 ,, | 17 ,, | **31** | 45 | 59 R. to Ferison LXX | 73 ,, |
| Ferio | 4 ,, | 18 ,, | **32** (33b27) | 46 | 60 R. to Datisi LXX | 74 ,, |
| Cesare | **5** (37a32) | **19** (37b19) | **33** | **47** (37b19) | 61 C. to 58 | **75** (38a26) |
| Camestres | **6** (37b11) | **20** | **34** (37b19) | 48 C. to 58 | **62** (37b19) | **76** |
| Festino | **7** (37b13) | **21** (37b39) | **35** | **49** (37b39) | 63 C. to 60 | **77** |
| Baroco | **8** (37b13) | **22** | **36** (37b39) | **50** | **64** (37b39) | **78** |
| Darapti | 9 C. to 3 | 23 C. to 17 | **37** | 51 | 65 C. to 59 | 79 C. to 73 |
| Felapton | 10 C. to 4 | 24 C. to 18 | **38** | 52 | 66 C. to 60 | 80 C. to 74 |
| Disamis | 11 C. to 3 | **25** | 39 C. to 17 | 53 C. to 59 | 67 | **81** |
| Datisi | 12 C. to 3 | 26 C. to 17 | **40** | 54 | 68 C. to 59 | 82 C. to 73 |
| Bocardo | 13 C.c. to 11 | **27** | **41** | 55 R. to Barbara LXL | **69** | **83** |
| Ferison | 14 C. to 4 | 28 C. to 18 | **42** | 56 | 70 C. to 60 | 84 C. to 74 |

*Notes to table 12 on pages 83 and 86*

TABLE 12 *continued*

| | *LQQ* | *QLX* | *LQX* | *QLM* | *LQM* |
|---|---|---|---|---|---|
| Barbara | **85** | **99** (35b26) | **113** | 127 | 141 R. to Baroco LLL |
| Celarent | **86** (35b30) | **100** (36a17) | 114 R. to Ferio LXL | 128 | 142 M.s. from 114 |
| Darii | **87** | **101** (35b26) | **115** (36a39) | 129 | 143 R. to Camestres LLL |
| Ferio | **88** (35b30) | **102** (36a39) | 116 R. to Celarent LXL | 130 | 144 |
| Cesare | **89** | **103** (38a26) | 117 R. to Ferio LXL | **131** (38a26) | 145 C. to 142 |
| Camestres | **90** (38b4) | 104 R. to Ferison LXL | **118** (38b4) | 132 C. to 142 | **146** (38b4) |
| Festino | **91** | **105** | 119 C. to 116 | **133** | 147 C. to 144 |
| Baroco | **92** (38b27) | **106** | **120** (38b27) | **134** | **148** (38b27) |
| Darapti | **93** | **107** | **121** | 135 | 149 C. to 143 |
| Felapton | **94** | **108** | 122 C. to 116 | 136 | 150 C. to 144 |
| Disamis | 95 C. to 73 | **109** | **123** | 137 C. to 143 | 151 |
| Datisi | **96** | **110** | **124** | 138 | 152 C. to 143 |
| Bocardo | **97** | **111** | 125 R. to Barbara XQM | 139 R. to Barbara LLL | 153 |
| Ferison | **98** | **112** | **126** | 140 | **154** |

moods with one universal premiss (39a28–31). Ross has $OAI$ in the third figure, though Bocardo is easily derivable by c.c.

29, 31 These moods are overlooked by Aristotle, though he doubtless regarded them as invalid. See Ross, p. 336.

43–46, 51, 52, 54, 56 All these moods are provable by modal subordination of the conclusion from $QXQ$ moods.

67 Provable by m.s. from 39.

85, 87 Aristotle gives only the indication (35b38–36a1, 36a39–b2) that Barbara and Darii with necessary major and contingent minor are proved by *reductio*. Hence 85 and 87 are probably invalid, since a *reductio* will not serve to prove any mood with a contingent conclusion.

104 Aristotle seems to be urging a *reductio* proof in 38a25–26, although Becker has C. to 114. Ross's R. to Darii $QXQ$ is surely wrong.

113 Aristotle proves Barbara $LQM$ but does not mention Barbara $LQX$, which we assume to be invalid.

125 Not in Becker.

127–130, 135, 136, 138, 140 Provable by m.s. from $QLQ$ moods.

139 Not in Becker.

141 Ross has R. to Bocardo $LXX$, which involves a more complicated proof.

144, 151, 153 By m.s. from 116, 95 and 125 respectively.

## 31. The $QQQ$ moods

We proceed now to deduce those contingent moods which are derivable in the $Q$–$L$–$X$–$M$ system.

200. Barbara $QQQ$
300. Celarent $QQQ$ (from 200 by c.c.)
201. Darii $QQQ$
301. Ferio $QQQ$ (from 201 by c.c.)
302. Darapti $QQQ$ (from 201 by c.)
303. Felapton $QQQ$ (from 301 by c.)
304. Disamis $QQQ$ (from 201 by c.)
305. Datisi $QQQ$ (from 304 by c.)
306. Bocardo $QQQ$ (from 304 by c.c.)
307. Ferison $QQQ$ (from 305 by c.c.)
308. Bramantip $QQQ$ (from 200 by subalternation and c.)
309. Dimaris $QQQ$ (from 304 by c.)

310. Fesapo *QQQ* (from 308 by c.c.)
311. Barbari *QQQ* (from 200 by sub.)
312. Celaront *QQQ* (from 300 by sub.)
313. Camenop *QQQ* (from 308 by c.c.)

There are in addition the following moods, validated by complementary conversion, which lack a valid *XXX* counterpart:

489–494. *AEA, EEA, AAE, EAA, AEE, EEE* in figure I (from Barbara and Celarent)
495–500. *AOI, EOI, AIO, EII, AOO, EOO* in figure I (from Darii and Ferio)
501–506. *AOI, EOI, AIO, EII, AOO, EOO* in figure III (from Datisi and Ferison)
507–512. *OEI, IEI, IAO, OAI, OEO, IEO* in figure III (from Disamis and Bocardo)
513–518. *EEI, AEI, AAO, EAI, EEO, AEO* in figure III (from Darapti and Felapton)
519–525. *OAO, IEI, OEI, IAO, OAI, IEO, OEO* in figure IV (from Dimaris)
526–530. *EEI, AAO, AEI, EAI, EEO* in figure IV (from Bramantip, Fesapo and Camenop)
531–536. *AEI, EEI, AAO, EAI, AEO, EEO* in figure I (from Barbari and Celaront)

In all, 64 *QQQ* moods are provable in the *Q–L–X–M* system, 16 of which have an *XXX* counterpart, and 48 by complementary conversion. By no means all these moods are to be found in Aristotle. But when we set aside moods systematically omitted from Aristotle's discussion – fourth figure moods, subaltern moods, and moods obtained by complementary conversion of the conclusion – we find a remarkably good correlation between *Q–L–X–M* moods and Aristotle's (see table 13, page 92). Only in the case where complementary conversion is required to arrive at every possible combination of premisses which yields a conclusion does Aristotle omit four valid moods, namely *EOI* in the first figure, and *AOI, IEI* and *AEI* in the third.

Objections have been urged by various philosophers against the validity of *QQQ* syllogisms. The principal objection seems to be that Aristotle fails to take account of the fact that, for a conclusion to be validly drawn, the premisses must be not only possible, but jointly possible. Consider, for example, the following syllogism from Occam. It is stated with possible rather than contingent premisses, but may be adapted to the latter, as a different version of it is in fact by Mrs. Kneale [1].

It is possible that everything coloured should be white.
It is possible that everything black should be coloured.
Therefore, it is possible that everything black should be white.

About this syllogism Occam says, "*Ista regula est falsa: Praemissae sunt possibiles, ergo conclusio est possibilis. Sed ista regula est vera: Si praemissae sunt possibiles et compossibiles, conclusio est possibilis*". Aristotle's rule, that what follows from the possible is itself possible (34a5–24), would therefore seem to stand in need of amendment, viz. that what follows from the *jointly* possible is itself possible.

## 32. The *QXQ* and *XQQ* moods

| | | |
|---|---|---|
| 314. | Barbara *QXQ* | (from 202 by c.c.) |
| 315. | Celarent *QXQ* | (from 202 by c.c.) |
| 203. | Darii *QXQ* | |
| 316. | Ferio *QXQ* | (from 203 by c.c.) |
| 317. | Darapti *QXQ* | (from 203 by c.) |
| 318. | Felapton *QXQ* | (from 316 by c.) |
| 319. | Datisi *QXQ* | (from 203 by c.) |
| 320. | Ferison *QXQ* | (from 316 by c.) |
| 321. | Barbari *QXQ* | (from 314 by sub.) |
| 322. | Celaront *QXQ* | (from 315 by sub.) |
| 323. | Darapti *XQQ* | (from 317 by c.) |
| 324. | Disamis *XQQ* | (from 319 by c.) |
| 325. | Bramantip *XQQ* | (from 321 by c.) |
| 326. | Dimaris *XQQ* | (from 324 by c.) |
| 327. | Camenop *XQQ* | (from 322 by c.) |

I shall not list those additional moods derivable by complementary conversion. There are 21 of them (including axiom 202),

[1] Occam, *Summa Logicae*, ed. Boehner, St. Bonaventure N.Y. 1951–4, III 1, chapt. 23, 9 ff; Kneale, p. 88.

but as only two of them, *IEI* from Disamis *XQQ* and *AEI* from Darapti *XQQ*, fall within the three Aristotelian figures and involve a different combination of premisses rather than merely a different conclusion, the Philosopher may be excused for having failed to mention them. However, there is some question about Darapti *XQQ*. Aristotle rightly observes (39b11–14) that if we convert Darapti's minor we get Darii with assertoric major and contingent minor, and he has already established (35a35–40) that this combination of premisses yields only a possible, not a contingent, conclusion. What he seems to have failed to notice is that if we convert the *major* of Darapti *XQQ* we get by means of Darii *QXQ* a conclusion which only requires conversion to become the original conclusion of Darapti *XQQ*: this is in fact his method of proving Disamis *XXX* in chapter 6. Apart from this, Aristotle's system of *QXQ*/*XQQ* moods coincides perfectly with that of the *Q–L–X–M* calculus.

## 33. The *QXM* and *XQM* moods

Instead of making a separate list of the *QXM*/*XQM* moods provable in the *Q–L–X–M* calculus, I shall summarize them in table 13. In addition to the axioms Barbara, Celarent and Ferio *XQM*, and those moods reducible to them by conversion, *QXM*/*XQM* moods are derivable from *QXQ*, *XQQ*, and, in the case of Festino *QXM*, Bocardo *QXM* and Darii *XQM*, *MXM*/*XMM* theses by modal subordination.

Aristotle's approach to these moods is somewhat different. In dealing with syllogisms with one contingent and one assertoric premiss he makes it clear that, in the first figure, whenever the *major* premiss is contingent the conclusion will be contingent, but when the *minor* is contingent the conclusion will be merely possible, not contingent (33b25 ff.). Furthermore these *XQM* moods are not perfect, but provable from other moods. His proof, which makes use of the principle that what is impossible cannot follow from what is merely false but not impossible, proceeds as follows in the case of Celarent *XQM* [1]:

[1] 34b19–25. This example is chosen rather than that of Barbara *XQM*, for the *reductio* syllogism of which Aristotle seems to employ the invalid

| | |
|---|---|
| If | No $B$ is $A$ |
| and | It is contingent that all $C$ is $B$ |
| then | It is possible that no $C$ is $A$. |
| For suppose | It is necessary that some $C$ is $A$ |
| then, since it is at most false | |
| but not impossible that | All $C$ is $B$ |
| it follows that | Some $B$ is $A$, |
| which *is* impossible. | |

Here Aristotle is using the mood Disamis $LXX$ to show that the contradictory of the conclusion of Celarent $XQM$, when combined with an hypothesis that is neither part of nor inconsistent with the premisses of Celarent $XQM$, entails a proposition that *is* inconsistent with these premisses. The contradictory of the conclusion must therefore be inconsistent with these premisses. This reasoning is fallacious. One might as well argue for the validity of the categorical $IAI$ in the first figure:

| | |
|---|---|
| If | Some $B$ is $A$ |
| and | All $C$ is $B$ |
| then | Some $C$ is $A$. |
| For suppose | No $C$ is $A$ |
| then, since it is at most | |
| false but not impossible that | All $B$ is $C$ |
| it follows that | No $B$ is $A$, |
| which *is* impossible. | |

Or, if this example is objected to on the grounds that the premisses of $IAI$ do not, while those of Celarent $XQM$ do, rule out the impossibility of the premiss subjoined to the *reductio* syllogism, a "proof" exactly similar to Aristotle's can be constructed for Baroco $XMM$, the latter being equivalent to the rejected Barbara $XLL$. However, the fact that we do not accept Aristotle's proof of Barbara, Celarent, Darii and Ferio $XQM$ does not mean that we should not accept them as valid moods, and they will be found

---

Bocardo $LXL$, while he need only have used Bocardo $LXX$. See Ross, pp. 338–9, where Aristotle's method of proof is defended against the criticisms of Becker and Tredennick.

in table 13. There is a close correlation between the *QXM/XQM* moods provable in the *Q–L–X–M* system and those held to be valid by Aristotle, only one of the former, Festino *QXM*, not being found among the latter.

## 34. The *QLQ* and *LQQ* moods

For those *QLQ* and *LQQ* moods provable in the *Q–L–X–M* calculus, see table 13. They are without exception derived from *QXQ* and *XQQ* theses by modal subordination. Aristotle, on the other hand, designates Barbara, Celarent, Darii and Ferio *QLQ* perfect syllogisms (35b23–26) and proves other moods from them by conversion. The agreement between the *Q–L–X–M* system and Aristotle's is good here, the only aberration being Darapti *LQQ*, a consequence of the disputed Darapti *XQQ*.

## 35. The *QLX* and *LQX* moods

These moods are derived in the *Q–L–X–M* system by *reductio* arguments from *QXM* and *XQM* moods. Aristotle too proves them by *reductio ad absurdum:* for example in 36a32–39 he proves Ferio *LQX* by reducing it to Cesare *LXL:*

| | |
|---|---|
| If | Necessarily no *B* is *A* |
| and | It is contingent that some *C* is *B* |
| then | Some *C* is not *A*. |
| For suppose | All *C* is *A* |
| then, since | Necessarily no *B* is *A* |
| it follows that | Necessarily no *C* is *B*, |
| which contradicts the original minor premiss. | |

Surprisingly enough, although he is fond of using *reductio* arguments, Aristotle proves no *QLX/LQX* moods by reducing them to *QXM/XQM* moods. For this reason there is a considerable number of the former – 14 in fact – which are provable from the latter in the *Q–L–X–M* system but are not found in Aristotle.

## 36. The *QLM* and *LQM* moods

Those of the *QLM*/*LQM* moods which are not provable in the *Q–L–X–M* system from *QLQ*/*LQQ* and *QLX*/*LQX* moods (Barbara *LQM*, Bocardo *QLM*) are provable from *LML*/*LMM* moods. The fact that there are 24 each of the latter makes the *QLM*/*LQM* moods "complete". Aristotle's system of these moods is, however, fragmentary – from at least 3 and probably 6 combinations of a necessary and a contingent premiss he would maintain that no conclusion at all follows. This further lack of Aristotelicity of the *Q–L–X–M* system is a consequence of Aristotle's failure to deduce the *reductio* counterparts of *QXM* and *XQM* moods.

TABLE 13

| | *QQQ* | *QXQ* | *XQQ* | *QXM* | *XQM* | *QLQ* | *LQQ* | *QLX* | *LQX* | *QLM* | *LQM* | *QQM* |
|---|---|---|---|---|---|---|---|---|---|---|---|---|
| Barbara | 200 | 314 | | 328 | 204 | 367 | | | | 424 | 448 | 472 |
| Celarent | 300 | 315 | | 329 | 205 | 368 | | **382** | 401 | 425 | 449 | 473 |
| Darii | 201 | 203 | | 330 | 350 | 369 | | **383** | **402** | 426 | 450 | 474 |
| Ferio | 301 | 316 | | 331 | 206 | 370 | | | 403 | 427 | 451 | 475 |
| Cesare | | | | | 351 | | | **384** | 404 | **428** | 452 | |
| Camestres | | | | 332 | | | | 385 | **405** | 429 | **453** | |
| Festino | | | | **333** | 352 | | | **386** | 406 | **430** | 454 | |
| Baroco | | | | | | | | **387** | **407** | **431** | **455** | |
| Darapti | 302 | 317 | **323** | 334 | 353 | 371 | **377** | **388** | **408** | 432 | 456 | 476 |
| Felapton | 303 | 318 | | 335 | 354 | 372 | | | 409 | 433 | 457 | 477 |
| Disamis | 304 | | 324 | 336 | 355 | | 378 | **389** | **410** | 434 | 458 | 478 |
| Datisi | 305 | 319 | | 337 | 356 | 373 | | **390** | **411** | 435 | 459 | 479 |
| Bocardo | 306 | | | 338 | | | | | 412 | 436 | 460 | 480 |
| Ferison | 307 | 320 | | 339 | 357 | 374 | | | **413** | 437 | **461** | 481 |
| Bramantip | 308 | | 325 | 340 | 358 | | 379 | 391 | 414 | 438 | 462 | 482 |
| Camenes | | | | 341 | 359 | | | 392 | 415 | 439 | 463 | 483 |
| Dimaris | 309 | | 326 | 342 | 360 | | 380 | 393 | 416 | 440 | 464 | 484 |
| Fresison | | | | 343 | 361 | | | 394 | 417 | 441 | 465 | |
| Fesapo | 310 | | | 344 | 362 | | | 395 | 418 | 442 | 466 | 485 |
| Barbari | 311 | 321 | | 345 | 363 | 375 | | 396 | 419 | 443 | 467 | 486 |
| Celaront | 312 | 322 | | 346 | 364 | 376 | | 397 | 420 | 444 | 468 | 487 |
| Cesaro | | | | 347 | 365 | | | 398 | 421 | 445 | 469 | |
| Camestrop | | | | 348 | | | | 399 | 422 | 446 | 470 | |
| Camenop | 313 | | 327 | 349 | 366 | | 381 | 400 | 423 | 447 | 471 | 488 |

## 37. Summary of the *Q-L-X-M* moods

Table 13, shown above, summarizes the *Q–L–X–M* system of contingent syllogisms with the exception of moods derivable by complementary conversion. Each of the moods provable as theses receives a separate number beginning at 300. Moods belonging to the three figures and to the eleven contingent syllogistic forms recognized by Aristotle fall within the rectangle of dotted lines, others without. Within the rectangle, *Q–L–X–M* moods which Aristotle either certainly or probably took to be invalid appear in bold face: they represent those un-Aristotelian features of table 13 which do not appear in table 12. There are no moods accepted as valid by Aristotle which fall outside the *Q–L–X–M* system.

In all, there are 24 non-Aristotelian *Q–L–X–M* moods, the existence of which is due to the following factors:

(a) Aristotle's failure to notice that *QLX*/*LQX* moods may be proved by reductio ad absurdum to *QXM*/*XQM* moods. This accounts for twelve missing *QLX*/*LQX* moods (nos. 383, 384, 386, 387, 389, 390, 402, 405, 407, 410, 411, 413), two more *QLX*/*LQX* moods derivable from them by subalternation (388, 408), and six *QLM*/*LQM* moods derivable by modal subordination (428, 430, 431, 453, 455, 461).

(b) Aristotle's omission of the proof of Darapti *XQQ* by conversion to Darii *QXQ*. This yields 323 and its modal subordinate 377.

(c) The fact (which we can excuse Aristotle for ignoring) that Festino *QXM* is a modal subordinate of Festino *MXM* of the *L–X–M* calculus. Hence it, 333, and its *reductio* mood 382 are *Q–L–X–M* theses.

These 24 non-Aristotelian moods, out of a total of 154 possible moods within the three Aristotelian figures and the eleven syllogistic forms, cause a drop in the Aristotelicity of the *Q–L–X–M* system to 85%, compared with the 100% of the *L–X–M* system. This figure is higher, however, than that which we would obtain if we constructed a system of contingent moods within the *L–X–M* calculus by using definitions *Q*9 and *Q*10 of page 74. This system would appear as follows, where the theses beginning at 800 are all consequences of axioms 1–14 of the *L–X–M* calculus.

| | *QQQ* | *QXQ* | *XQQ* | *QXM* | *XQM* | *QLQ* | *LQQ* | *QLX* | *LQX* | *QLM* | *LQM* |
|---|---|---|---|---|---|---|---|---|---|---|---|
| Barbara | 800 | 810 | | 820 | 834 | 848 | | **858** | **872** | 886 | 900 |
| Celarent | 801 | 811 | | 821 | 835 | 849 | | **859** | 873 | 887 | 901 |
| Darii | 802 | 812 | | 822 | 836 | 850 | | **860** | **874** | 888 | 902 |
| Ferio | 803 | 813 | | 823 | 837 | 851 | | **861** | 875 | 889 | 903 |
| Cesare | | | | **824** | 838 | | | **862** | 876 | **890** | 904 |
| Camestres | | | | 825 | **839** | | | 863 | **877** | 891 | **905** |
| Festino | | | | **826** | 840 | | | **864** | 878 | **892** | 906 |
| Baroco | | | | **827** | **841** | | | **865** | **879** | **893** | **907** |
| Darapti | 804 | 814 | | 828 | 842 | 852 | | **866** | **880** | 894 | 908 |
| Felapton | 805 | 815 | | 829 | 843 | 853 | | **867** | 881 | 895 | 909 |
| Disamis | 806 | **816** | A | 830 | 844 | **854** | A | **868** | **882** | 896 | 910 |
| Datisi | 807 | 817 | | 831 | 845 | 855 | | **869** | **883** | 897 | 911 |
| Bocardo | 808 | **818** | | 832 | **846** | **856** | | **870** | 884 | 898 | 912 |
| Ferison | 809 | 819 | | 833 | 847 | 857 | | **871** | **885** | 899 | **913** |

Among these contingent moods there are 37 not recognized by Aristotle, and in addition 2 (marked "A") are recognized by him but missing in the system. The degree of correlation of the system with Aristotle's is 75%.

I shall not attempt to construct a decision procedure for the *Q–L–X–M* calculus, not because it would be impossible, but because the system is perhaps too *ad hoc* to be of much formal logical interest. One of the problems involved in the construction would be that of dealing with the formulae *NQAab* and *NQIab*. In the *L–X–M* calculus the negation of a simple expression is itself a simple expression, and the above formulae would presumably have to be admitted as new simple *Q–L–X–M* expressions, thus complicating the syllogistic. Of course, if we define the contingent in terms of necessity, actuality and possibility – i.e. define the operator *Q* in terms of *L* and *M* or in simpler terms – then the decision procedure of the *L–X–M* calculus will provide a decision procedure for formulae containing *Q*. But we have seen that no definition of *Q* in terms of *L* and *M*, or otherwise, allows us to reproduce the structure of Aristotle's contingent syllogisms as well as does their derivation from separate axioms.

It will be noted that *QQM* moods are included in table 13 for the sake of completeness. Although Aristotle never mentions them, one of them is provable by subordination from each *QQQ* mood, and 483. Camenes *QQM* from 473. Celarent *QQM* by conversion. The following are the totals of the various *Q–L–X–M* moods provable in the different categories, including those provable by complementary conversion:

| | | | |
|---|---|---|---|
| *QQQ* moods: | 16 + 48 by c.c. | = | 64 |
| *QXQ/XQQ* moods: | 15 + 21 | = | 36 |
| *QXM/XQM* moods: | 42 + 42 | = | 84 |
| *QLQ/LQQ* moods: | 15 + 21 | = | 36 |
| *QLX/LQX* moods: | 42 + 42 | = | 84 |
| *QLM/LQM* moods: | 48 + 48 | = | 96 |
| *QQM* moods: | 17 + 47 | = | 64 |
| Total moods containing *Q*: | | | 464 |
| Pure *L–X–M* moods: | | | 333 |
| Total *Q–L–X–M* moods: | | | 797. |

## 38. Conclusion

The purpose of this book has been to show that Aristotle's system of modal syllogisms exhibits a higher degree of logical consistency than most of his successors have given him credit for. His system of apodeictic moods has been axiomatized in a purely formal calculus whose theorems coincide perfectly with Aristotle's intuitions. This calculus can be shown to be complete in the sense that every formula not provable from its axioms may be demonstrably rejected on the basis of certain axiomatic rejections. Not so much success has greeted the attempt to provide a formal counterpart to Aristotle's system of contingent moods, the degree of correlation of the two systems being only 85%, but this figure is nonetheless higher than that exhibited by, for example, a system such as Łukasiewicz's.

In those matters which have classically been the subject of dispute among his followers, Aristotle's original teachings have been shown to be perfectly defensible. Even such vexed issues as the validity of Barbaras *LXL* and *XLL*, complementary conversion, and the inconvertibility of *QEab* can all be decided in Aristotle's favour in the sense that his doctrines can be seen as parts of a logically consistent whole. This whole, which has revealed some unsuspected elegancies of a purely formal nature, has been constructed on the basis of a rather large and inelegant collection of axioms, but this method of construction has been deemed preferable to the method of basing Aristotle's system on laws of propositional modal logic. No doubt this latter method would be neater, but, as has been shown, the use of such laws as *CCpqCLpLq* and *CQpQNp* leads to results which Aristotle himself would not accept.

This last point provides an opportunity to reply to one final criticism of Aristotle. In her discussion of the *Organon* Mrs. Kneale propounds the following dilemma for Aristotle's followers [1]. If modal words modify predicates or terms there is no need for a theory of *modal* syllogisms, since the latter will merely be ordinary assertoric syllogisms with peculiar terms. If, on the other hand, modal words modify whole statements, there is no need for a theory of modal *syllogisms*, since the logical relations between modalized statements are determined entirely by the modal logic of unanalysed propositions. In either case, modal syllogistic is otiose.

The reply to this criticism might be as follows. Certainly, modal syllogistic is not simply a branch of assertoric syllogistic; i.e. assertoric syllogistic with modalized terms. At least, to make it so entirely destroys the character of Aristotle's system (see sect. 8). On the other hand, we cannot be sure that in Aristotle's system modal words can be taken as qualifying whole statements either. For his modal syllogisms seem to defy treatment in propositional terms: the propositional modal laws put forward are too coarse to catch the fine distinctions Aristotle makes between valid and invalid syllogisms. We are left with three possibilities. Either (a) Aristotle's intuitions concerning validity and invalidity were hopelessly muddled and wrong-headed – this possibility we have chosen to set aside if for no other reason than that the remarkable coherence of his very complex system does not indicate muddle-headedness. Or (b) the alternatives for a modal word to "modify a term" or "modify a proposition" are not exhaustive. Or (c), and this is perhaps the most attractive possibility, modal syllo-

---

[1] Kneale, p. 91.

gistic presents the logician with a challenge to produce modal propositional laws which *do* satisfy Aristotle's intuitions.

Let me give one example of the latter. It was seen that the law *CQpQNp* did not allow for the Aristotelian implication *C QAab QEab*. Now *Aab* and *Eab* are contraries, not contradictories. Hence let us see if it is possible to construct a propositional logic containing a logical operator *R* which denotes contrariety [1]; we would then, in place of *CQpQNp*, have *CQpQRp*, and, for the subcontraries *Iab* and *Oab*, *CQpQNRNp*. I do not know whether such an approach would yield worthwhile results. But if it did, then Aristotle's modal syllogistic could at least be viewed as providing the incentive to construct new and more sophisticated propositional modal logics.

---

[1] See my forthcoming paper *Contrariety*, in which the possibilities of constructing such a logic are explored.

# INDEX

Abailard, 3.
Albert the Great, 3, 68.
Aldrich, H., 4, 28.
Alexander of Aphrodisias, 2, 15, 16n, 17n, 81, 82.
al-Farabi, 2.
Ammonius, 67n.
Ariston the Alexandrian, 28n.
Aristotle, *Prior analytics*, 1, 2, 3, 6–8, 10, 12, 13, 17, 19, 22, 23, 28n, 31–33, 36, 39–42, 45n, 48, 66, 68–71, 73, 78–86, 88, 89, 91.
*Posterior analytics*, 22.
*De interpretatione*, 31, 33, 66.
Austin, J. L., 6n.
Averroes, 3, 17n, 68.
Avicenna, 3.
Becker-Freyseng, A., 4, 5, 9n, 18–22, 67, 68n, 69, 71, 78n, 79n, 83, 86, 90n.
Bochenski, I. M., 2, 3, 5, 6n, 16, 18, 19n, 28n, 35n, 67n, 68n, 73n, 82n.
Boethius, 67.
Cauchy, V., 74n.
Couturat, L., 29n.
Duns Scotus, 3.
Eudemus, 2.
Galen, 3.
Henle, P., 8n.
Hintikka, J., 13–15.
Keckermann, B., 4.
Keynes, J. N., 4.
Kneale, M., 3n, 81n, 82, 88, 96.
Kneale, W., 3n.
Leibniz, 29n.
Lemmon, E. J., and Gjertsen, 70n.
Leśniewski, S., 69.
Lewis, C. I., 21, 32, 70n.
Łukasiewicz, J., 1, 4–6, 11, 12n, 15, 16, 22, 29–32, 35–39n, 45–49, 51, 52, 67, 69, 76, 82, 95.

MacColl, H., 68.
Madkour, I., 3n.
Miller, J. W., 30n.
Occam, William, 3, 88.
Peter of Mantua, 28n.
Peter of Spain, 6n.
Prior, A. N., 6n, 69, 70n.
Pseudo-Scotus, 73n.
Reid, Thomas, 4.
Rescher, N., 2n, 5, 21–25.
Rondelet, A., 81.
Ross, W. D., 2n, 8, 9n, 11, 16n, 17n, 22, 28n, 66, 67, 70, 71, 78, 79n, 83, 86, 90n.
Shepherdson, J. C., 30n.
Słupecki, J., 30, 48, 49, 53, 54.
Sugihara, T., 21.
Theophrastus, 1–3, 15–18, 81, 82.
Tredennick, H., 90n.
Venn, J., 30.
Victorinus, Marius, 67.
von Wright, G. H., 21.
Whately, R., 4.